# Student Edition

# Eureka Math
# Grade 3
# Modules 6 & 7

Gary Chen

Special thanks go to the Gordon A. Cain Center and to the Department of Mathematics at Louisiana State University for their support in the development of *Eureka Math*.

Name _Gary_                                    Date _5/23/17_

1.  "What is your favorite color?"  Survey the class to complete the tally chart below.

| Favorite Colors | |
| --- | --- |
| **Color** | **Number of Students** |
| Green |  |
| Yellow | \| |
| Red | ~~\|\|\|\|~~ |
| Blue | ~~\|\|\|\|~~ ~~\|\|\|\|~~ \|\|\| |
| Orange | \|\|\| |

2.  Use the tally chart to answer the following questions.

   a.  How many students chose orange as their favorite color?

   3

   b.  How many students chose yellow as their favorite color?

   1

   c.  Which color did students choose the most?  How many students chose it?

   Blue – 13 votes

   d.  Which color did students choose the least?  How many students chose it?

   Green – 0 votes

   e.  What is the difference between the number of students in parts (c) and (d)?  Write a number sentence to show your thinking.    13-0=13

   The difference between Blue and Green is 13

   f.  Write an equation to show the total number of students surveyed on this chart.

3.  Use the tally chart in Problem 1 to complete the picture graphs below.

    a.

| Favorite Colors | | | | |
|---|---|---|---|---|
| Green | Yellow | Red | Blue | Orange |

Each ♡ represents 1 student.

    b.

| Favorite Colors | | | | |
|---|---|---|---|---|
| Green | Yellow | Red | Blue | Orange |

Each ♡ represents 2 students.

4. Use the picture graph in Problem 3(b) to answer the following questions.

   a. What does each ♡ represent?

      2 students

   b. Draw a picture and write a number sentence to show how to represent 3 students in your picture graph.

      ♡♡     2+1=3

   c. How many students does ♡ ♡ ♡ ♡ ♡ ♡ ♡ represent?  Write a number sentence to show how you know.

      ♡=2

      2×7♡=14

   d. How many more ♡ did you draw for the color that students chose the most than for the color that students chose the least?  Write a number sentence to show the difference between the number of votes for the color that students chose the most and the color that students chose the least.

      Blue has 13 more than Green

      $\begin{array}{r} 13 \\ -\ 0 \\ \hline 13 \end{array}$   ♡♡♡♡♡♡

This page intentionally left blank

Name _____     Date _____

1.  The tally chart below shows a survey of students' favorite pets.  Each tally mark represents 1 student.

| Favorite Pets | |
|---|---|
| Pets | Number of Pets |
| Cats | ////-/ |
| Turtles | //// |
| Fish | // |
| Dogs | ////- /// |
| Lizards | // |

The chart shows a total of ___22___ students.

2.  Use the tally chart in Problem 1 to complete the picture graph below.  The first one has been done for you.

| Favorite Pets | | | | |
|---|---|---|---|---|

Each ◯ represents 1 student.

a.  The same number of students picked ___Fish___ and ___Lizards___ as their favorite pet.

b.  How many students picked dogs as their favorite pet?

8 students

c.  How many more students chose cats than turtles as their favorite pet?

2 students

3. Use the tally chart in Problem 1 to complete the picture graph below.

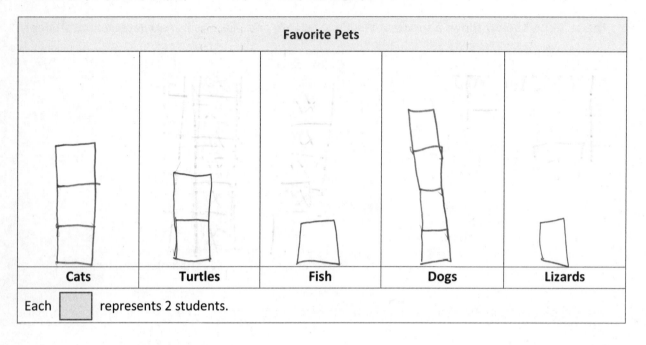

| Favorite Pets | | | | |
|---|---|---|---|---|
| Cats | Turtles | Fish | Dogs | Lizards |

Each ☐ represents 2 students.

a. What does each ☐ represent?

2 students

b. How many students does ☐☐☐☐☐ represent? Write a number sentence to show how you know.

5 × 2 = 10 students

c. How many more ☐ did you draw for dogs than for fish? Write a number sentence to show how many more students chose dogs than fish.

$$\begin{array}{r} 8 \\ -2 \\ \hline 6 \text{ students} \end{array}$$

Lesson 1:   Generate and organize data.

©2015 Great Minds. eureka-math.org
G3-M6-SE-B4-1.3.1-01.2016

Name _____    Date 5/24/17

1.  Find the total number of stamps each student has.  Draw tape diagrams with a unit size of 4 to show the number of stamps each student has.  The first one has been done for you.

Dana

Tanisha

Raquel

Anna

Each [stamp] represents 1 stamp.

Dana: | 4 | 4 | 4 | 4 |

Tanisha: | 4 | 4 |

Raquel: | 4 | 4 | 4 | 4 | 4 | 4 |

Anna: | 4 | 4 | 4 | 4 | 4 | 4 | 4 | 4 |

2.  Explain how you can create vertical tape diagrams to show this data.

You can create a vertical tape diagram by simply drawing the squares vertically.

3.   Complete the vertical tape diagrams below using the data from Problem 1.

a.

Dana     Tanisha     Raquel     Anna

b.

Dana     Tanisha     Raquel     Anna

c.   What is a good title for the vertical tape diagrams?

stamps Collected

d.   How many total units of 4 are in the vertical tape diagrams in Problem 3(a)?

20 units of 4.

e.   How many total units of 8 are in the vertical tape diagrams in Problem 3(b)?

10 units of 8.

f.   Compare your answers to parts (d) and (e).  Why does the number of units change?

The number of the unit changes because when you double the number of the units in the tape diagram it makes lessunits.

g.   Mattaeus looks at the vertical tape diagrams in Problem 3(b) and finds the total number of Anna's and Raquel's stamps by writing the equation 7 × 8 = 56.  Explain his thinking.

Mattaeus counted the number of units for Anna and Raquel, which is 7 and multiplied that by the value of each unit, 8

Name _____   Date 5/23/17

1.  Adi surveys third graders to find out their favorite fruits.  The results are in the table below.

| Favorite Fruits of Third Graders | |
| --- | --- |
| Fruit | Number of Student Votes |
| Banana | 8 |
| Apple | 16 |
| Strawberry | 12 |
| Peach | 4 |

Draw units of 2 to complete the tape diagrams to show the total votes for each fruit.  The first one has been done for you.

Banana:

| 2 | 2 | 2 | 2 |
| --- | --- | --- | --- |

Apple:

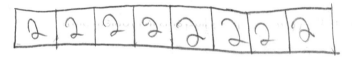

Strawberry:

Peach:

2.  Explain how you can create vertical tape diagrams to show this data.

You can create a vertical tape diagram by turning the
data

3.  Complete the vertical tape diagrams below using the data from Problem 1.

a.

| 2 |
| 2 |
| 2 |
| 2 |

Banana    Apple    Strawberry    Peach
4        8        6

b.

| 4 |
| 4 |

Banana    Apple    Strawberry    Peach
4        3

a   each Box represents 2 votes favorite fruits

b   "    "    "      4 votes

c.  What is a good title for the vertical tape diagrams?

Counting Fruits.

d.  Compare the number of units used in the vertical tape diagrams in Problems 3(a) and 3(b).  Why does the number of units change?

It changes because when the squares of the tape diagram grow then the units goes, they have not that much

e.  Write a multiplication number sentence to show the total number of votes for strawberry in the vertical tape diagram in Problem 3(a).

2×6=12

f.  Write a multiplication number sentence to show the total number of votes for strawberry in the vertical tape diagram in Problem 3(b).

4×3=12

g.  What changes in your multiplication number sentences in Problems 3(e) and (f)?  Why?

The multiplication problem changes because the boxes represent different amounts.

Lesson 2:     Rotate tape diagrams vertically.

EUREKA MATH

©2015 Great Minds. eureka-math.org
G3-M6-SE-B4-1.3.1-01.2016

Name _____          Date 5/25/16

1.  This table shows the number of students in each class.

| Number of Students in Each Class | |
| --- | --- |
| Class | Number of Students |
| Baking | 9 |
| Sports | 16 |
| Chorus | 13 |
| Drama | 18 |

Use the table to color the bar graph.  The first one has been done for you.

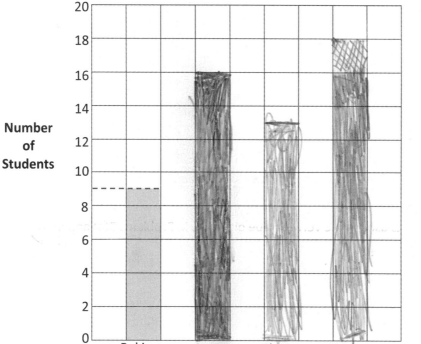

**Number of Students in Each Class**

a.  What is the value of each square in the bar graph?

2

b.  Write a number sentence to find how many total students are enrolled in classes.

9 + 16 + 13 + 18 = 54

c.  How many fewer students are in sports than in chorus and baking combined?  Write a number sentence to show your thinking.

6 students

2. This bar graph shows Kyle's savings from February to June. Use a straightedge to help you read the graph.

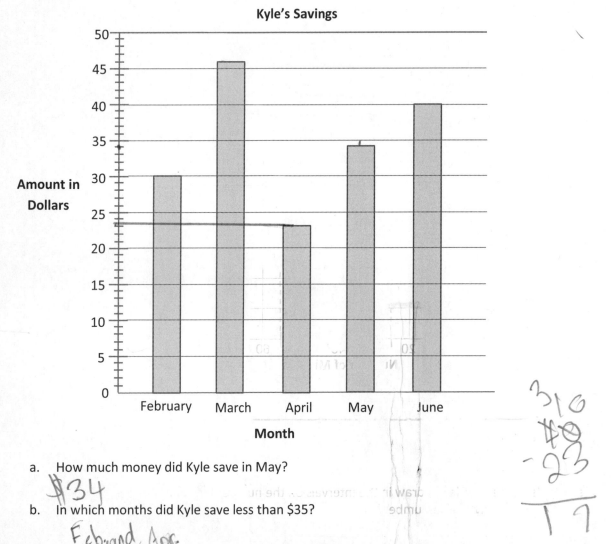

**Kyle's Savings**

a. How much money did Kyle save in May?

$34

b. In which months did Kyle save less than $35?

Feb. and Apr.

c. How much more did Kyle save in June than April? Write a number sentence to show your thinking.

$17

d. The money Kyle saved in ___April___ was half the money he saved in ___March___.

3. Complete the table below to show the same data given in the bar graph in Problem 2.

| Months | February | March | April | May | June |
|---|---|---|---|---|---|
| Amount Saved in Dollars | 30 | 46 | 23 | 34 | 40 |

Lesson 3:   Create scaled bar graphs.

©2015 Great Minds. eureka-math.org
G3-M6-SE-B4-1.3.1-01.2016

This bar graph shows the number of minutes Charlotte read from Monday through Friday.

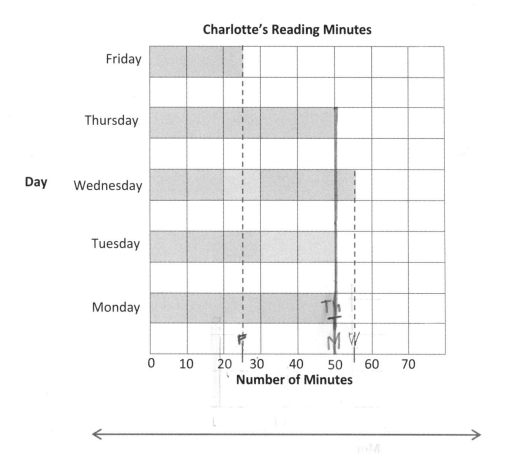

**Charlotte's Reading Minutes**

4. Use the graph's lines as a ruler to draw in the intervals on the number line shown above. Then plot and label a point for each day on the number line.

5. Use the graph or number line to answer the following questions.

   a. On which days did Charlotte read for the same number of minutes? How many minutes did Charlotte read on these days?

   Thurday, Tuesday, and Monday    50 min

   b. How many more minutes did Charlotte read on Wednesday than on Friday?

   30 min    55
              -25
              ___
              30

This page intentionally left blank

Name _____          Date 5/25/17

1.  This table shows the favorite subjects of third graders at Cayuga Elementary.

| Favorite Subjects | |
| --- | --- |
| Subject | Number of Student Votes |
| Math | 18 |
| ELA | 13 |
| History | 17 |
| Science | ? |

Use the table to color the bar graph.

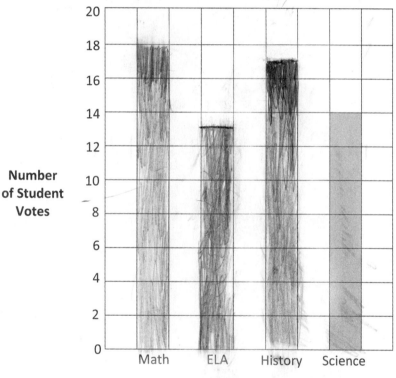

**Favorite Subjects**

a.  How many students voted for science?

14 students

b.  How many more students voted for math than for science?  Write a number sentence to show your thinking.

18-14= 4 students

c.  Which gets more votes, math and ELA together or history and science together?  Show your work.

18+13=31.          17+14=31          Neither one has more
                                      votes because 18+13=
                                      31 and 17+14=31.

```
 1
18
+13
───
31
```

```
17
+14
───
31
```

2.  This bar graph shows the number of liters of water Skyler uses this month.

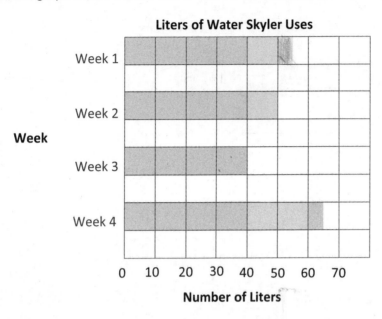

**Liters of Water Skyler Uses**

a.  During which week does Skyler use the most water? _Week 4_
    The least? _Week 3_

b.  How many more liters does Skyler use in Week 4 than Week 2?

    15 L    65-50 = 15 L

c.  Write a number sentence to show how many liters of water Skyler uses during Weeks 2 and 3 combined.

    90L    50L + 40L = 90L

d.  How many liters does Skyler use in total?    10L + 90L = 100L + (50L + 60L)
                                                            = 110L
    100L    W2 + W3    5L    W1    W4  5L
            50L + 40=90L   55  50L  65  60L

e.  If Skyler uses 60 liters in each of the 4 weeks next month, will she use more or less than she uses this month? Show your work.

    She will use less because 110 ⊘ 60.

    110 ⊘ 60

EUREKA
MATH™

3. Complete the table below to show the data displayed in the bar graph in Problem 2.

| Liters of Water Skyler Uses | |
|---|---|
| Week | Liters of Water |
| 1 | 55 |
| 2 | 50 |
| 3 | 40 |
| 4 | 65 |

This page  intentionally left  blank

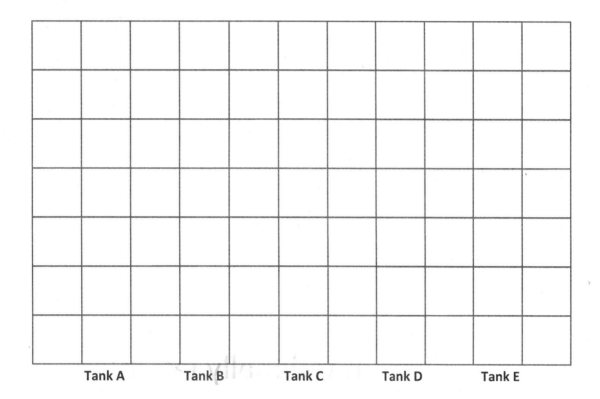

Tank A        Tank B        Tank C        Tank D        Tank E

**Tank**

graph A

©2015 Great Minds. eureka-math.org
G3-M6-SE-B4-1.3.1-01.2016

**Number of Fish at Sal's Pet Store**

Tank E

Tank D

Tank

Tank C

Tank B

Tank A

**Number of Fish**

graph B

     **Lesson 3:**     Create scaled bar graphs.

Name _____    Date 6/5/17

1.  The chart below shows the number of magazines sold by each student.

| Student | Ben | Rachel | Jeff | Stanley | Debbie |
|---|---|---|---|---|---|
| Magazines Sold | 300 | 250 | 100 | 450 | 600 |

a.  Use the chart to draw a bar graph below.  Create an appropriate scale for the graph.

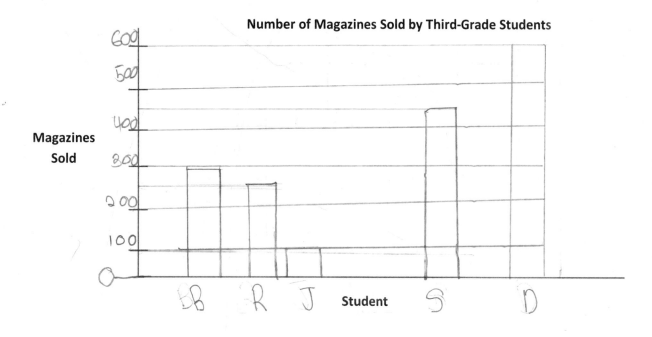

**Number of Magazines Sold by Third-Grade Students**

b.  Explain why you chose the scale for the graph.

c.  How many fewer magazines did Debbie sell than Ben and Stanley combined?

300 × 450 = 750 - 600 = 150 magazines

d.  How many more magazines did Debbie and Jeff sell than Ben and Rachel?

600 × 100 = 700      250 × 300 = 550

2.  The bar graph shows the number of visitors to a carnival from Monday through Friday.

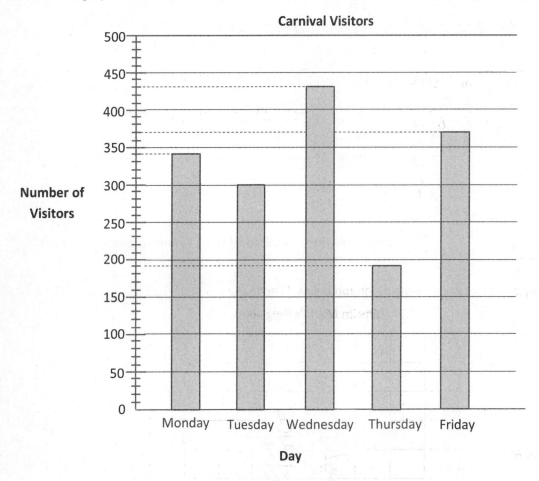

a.  How many fewer visitors were there on the least busy day than on the busiest day?

$$3 \overset{13}{\cancel{4}}\overset{}{8}0$$
$$-190$$
$$\overline{220}$$

$$430-190=220$$

b.  How many more visitors attended the carnival on Monday and Tuesday combined than on Thursday and Friday combined?

$$340+300=640 \quad \overset{5\,14}{6\cancel{4}\cancel{0}} \quad 190+370=560$$
$$\phantom{340+300=640}-560$$
$$\phantom{340+300=6}\overline{\phantom{4}80} \quad \begin{array}{r} 190 \\ +370 \\ \hline 560 \end{array}$$

**Lesson 4:**    Solve one- and two-step problems involving graphs.

Name _____     Date 6/6/17

1.  Maria counts the coins in her piggy bank and records the results in the tally chart below.  Use the tally marks to find the total number of each coin.

| Coins in Maria's Piggy Bank | | |
| --- | --- | --- |
| Coin | Tally | Number of Coins |
| Penny | //// //// //// //// //// //// //// //// //// //// //// //// //// /// | 68 |
| Nickel | //// //// //// //// //// //// //// //// //// //// //// //// // | 62 |
| Dime | //// //// //// //// //// //// //// //// //// //// //// // | 57 |
| Quarter | //// //// //// //// //// | 24 |

a.  Use the tally chart to complete the bar graph below.  The scale is given.

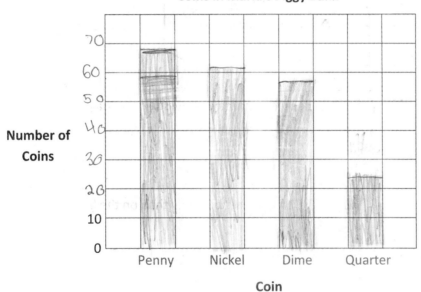

**Coins in Maria's Piggy Bank**

Number of Coins

70
60
50
40
30
20
10
0

Penny     Nickel     Dime     Quarter

Coin

b.  How many more pennies are there than dimes?

68 pennies
-57 dimes
11 pennies

c.  Maria donates 10 of each type of coin to charity.  How many total coins does she have left?  Show your work.

68
+62
130

130
+57
187

187
+24
211

211
-40
171

2.  Ms. Hollmann's class goes on a field trip to the planetarium with Mr. Fiore's class.  The number of students in each class is shown in the picture graphs below.

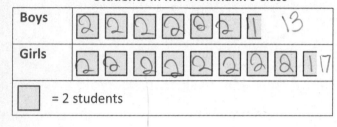

**Students in Ms. Hollmann's Class**

| Boys  | 2 2 2 2 2 2 1  13 |
| Girls | 2 2 2 2 2 2 2 2 1  17 |

☐ = 2 students

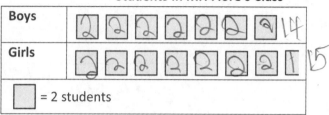

**Students in Mr. Fiore's Class**

| Boys  | 2 2 2 2 2 2 2 14 |
| Girls | 2 2 2 2 2 2 2 1  15 |

☐ = 2 students

a.  How many fewer boys are on the trip than girls?

$$13 + (17 + 15) - (13 + 14) = 5$$
$$32 - 29 = 5 - 27$$

b.  It costs $2 for each student to attend the field trip.  How much money does it cost for all students to attend?

```
  13
  17
  14
+ 15
 ‾‾‾‾
  59
```
59 + 59 = $118

c.  The cafeteria in the planetarium has 9 tables with 8 seats at each table.  Counting students and teachers, how many empty seats should there be when the 2 classes eat lunch?

$$9 \times 8 = 72$$
$$-59$$
13 empty seats.

EUREKA
MATH

graph

Lesson 4: Solve one- and two-step problems involving graphs.

25

©2015 Great Minds. eureka-math.org
G3-M6-SE-B4-1.3.1-01.2016

This page intentionally left blank

Name _____ Date _____

1. Use the ruler you made to measure different classmates' straws to the nearest inch, $\frac{1}{2}$ inch, and $\frac{1}{4}$ inch. Record the measurements in the chart below. Draw a star next to measurements that are exact.

| Straw Owner | Measured to the nearest inch | Measured to the nearest $\frac{1}{2}$ inch | Measured to the nearest $\frac{1}{4}$ inch |
|---|---|---|---|
| My straw | | | |
| | | | |
| | | | |
| | | | |
| | | | |
| | | | |
| | | | |

a. _____'s straw is the shortest straw I measured. It measures _____ inch(es).

b. _____'s straw is the longest straw I measured. It measures _____ inches.

c. Choose the straw from your chart that was most accurately measured with the $\frac{1}{4}$-inch intervals on your ruler. How do you know the $\frac{1}{4}$-inch intervals are the most accurate for measuring this straw?

©2015 Great Minds. eureka-math.org
G3-M6-SE-B4-1.3.1-01.2016

2.  Jenna marks a 5-inch paper strip into equal parts as shown below.

a.  Label the whole and half inches on the paper strip.

b.  Estimate to draw the $\frac{1}{4}$-inch marks on the paper strip.  Then, fill in the blanks below.

   1 inch is equal to _____ half inches.

   1 inch is equal to _____ quarter inches.

   1 half inch is equal to _____ quarter inches.

c.  Describe how Jenna could use this paper strip to measure an object that is longer than 5 inches.

3.  Sari says her pencil measures 8 half inches.  Bart disagrees and says it measures 4 inches.  Explain to Bart why the two measurements are the same in the space below.  Use words, pictures, or numbers.

        **Lesson 5:**     Create ruler with 1-inch, ½-inch, and ¼-inch intervals, and generate measurement data.

©2015 Great Minds. eureka-math.org
G3-M6-SE-B4-1.3.1-01.2016

Name _____     Date _____

1.  Travis measured 5 different-colored pencils to the nearest inch, $\frac{1}{2}$ inch, and $\frac{1}{4}$ inch.  He records the measurements in the chart below.  He draws a star next to measurements that are exact.

| Colored Pencil | Measured to the nearest inch | Measured to the nearest $\frac{1}{2}$ inch | Measured to the nearest $\frac{1}{4}$ inch |
|---|---|---|---|
| Red | 7 | $6\frac{1}{2}$ | $6\frac{3}{4}$ |
| Blue | 5 | 5 | $5\frac{1}{4}$ |
| Yellow | 6 | $5\frac{1}{2}$ ☆ | $5\frac{1}{2}$ ☆ |
| Purple | 5 | $4\frac{1}{2}$ | $4\frac{3}{4}$ |
| Green | 2 | 3 | $1\frac{3}{4}$ |

a.  Which colored pencil is the longest? _____

It measures _____ inches.

b.  Look carefully at Travis's data.  Which colored pencil most likely needs to be measured again?  Explain how you know.

EUREKA MATH™

Lesson 5:     Create ruler with 1-inch, ½-inch, and ¼-inch intervals, and generate measurement data.

29

2.  Evelyn marks a 4-inch paper strip into equal parts as shown below.

a.  Label the whole and half inches on the paper strip.

b.  Estimate to draw the $\frac{1}{4}$-inch marks on the paper strip.  Then, fill in the blanks below.

1 inch is equal to _____ half inches.

1 inch is equal to _____ quarter inches

1 half inch is equal to _____ quarter inches.

2 quarter inches are equal to _____ half inch.

3.  Travis says his yellow pencil measures $5\frac{1}{2}$ inches.  Ralph says that is the same as 11 half inches.  Explain how they are both correct.

30          Lesson 5:        Create ruler with 1-inch, ½-inch, and ¼-inch intervals, and generate
                              measurement data.

EUREKA
MATH

lined paper

**Lesson 5:** Create ruler with 1-inch, ½-inch, and ¼-inch intervals, and generate measurement data.

©2015 Great Minds. eureka-math.org
G3-M6-SE-B4-1.3.1-01.2016

This page intentionally left blank

Name _____  Date _____

1. Coach Harris measures the heights of the children on his third-grade basketball team in inches. The heights are shown on the line plot below.

**Heights of Children on Third-Grade Basketball Team**

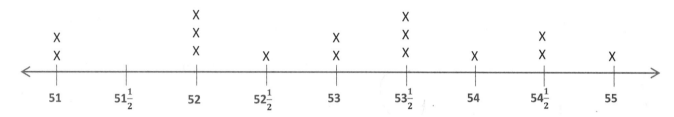

**Height in Inches**          X = 1 child

a. How many children are on the team? How do you know?

X = 1 child
15 children

b. How many children are less than 53 inches tall?

6 children

c. Coach Harris says that the most common height for the children on his team is $53\frac{1}{2}$ inches. Is he right? Explain your answer.

d. Coach Harris says that the player who does the tip-off in the beginning of the game has to be at least 54 inches tall. How many children could do the tip-off?

4 children

2.  Miss Vernier's class is studying worms.  The lengths of the worms in inches are shown in the line plot below.

**Lengths of Worms**

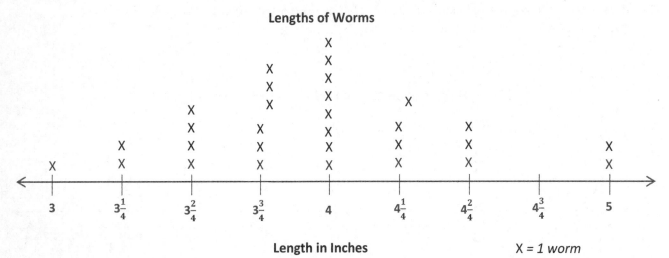

Length in Inches                          X = 1 worm

a.  How many worms did the class measure?  How do you know?

b.  Cara says that there are more worms $3\frac{3}{4}$ inches long than worms that are $3\frac{2}{4}$ and $4\frac{1}{4}$ inches long combined.  Is she right?  Explain your answer.

c.  Madeline finds a worm hiding under a leaf.  She measures it, and it is $4\frac{3}{4}$ inches long.  Plot the length of the worm on the line plot.

**Lesson 6:**    Interpret measurement data from various line plots.          **EUREKA MATH**

Name _____      Date _____

1.  Ms. Leal measures the heights of the students in her kindergarten class.  The heights are shown on the line plot below.

**Heights of Students in Ms. Leal's Kindergarten Class**

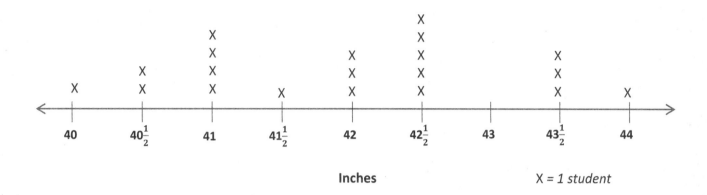

**Inches**                                    X = 1 student

a.  How many students in Ms. Leal's class are exactly 41 inches tall?

b.  How many students are in Ms. Leal's class?  How do you know?

c.  How many students in Ms. Leal's class are more than 42 inches tall?

d.  Ms. Leal says that for the class picture students in the back row must be at least $42\frac{1}{2}$ inches tall.  How many students should be in the back row?

2. Mr. Stein's class is studying plants. They plant seeds in clear plastic bags and measure the lengths of the roots. The lengths of the roots in inches are shown in the line plot below.

**Lengths of Plants' Roots**

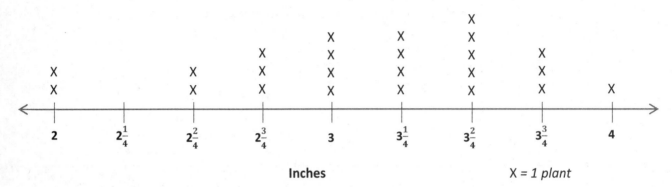

Inches                                    X = 1 plant

a. How many roots did Mr. Stein's class measure? How do you know?

b. Teresa says that the 3 most frequent measurements in order from shortest to longest are $3\frac{1}{4}$ inches, $3\frac{2}{4}$ inches, and $3\frac{3}{4}$ inches. Do you agree? Explain your answer.

c. Gerald says that the most common measurement is 14 quarter inches. Is he right? Why or why not?

Lesson 6:    Interpret measurement data from various line plots.

EUREKA
MATH

**Time Spent Outside Over the Weekend**

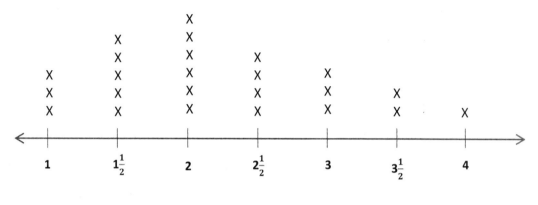

Hours

X = 1 person

time spent outside line plot

©2015 Great Minds. eureka-math.org
G3-M6-SE-B4-1.3.1-01.2016

This page intentionally left blank

Name _____  Date _____

Mrs. Weisse's class grows beans for a science experiment.  The students measure the heights of their bean plants to the nearest $\frac{1}{4}$ inch and record the measurements as shown below.

| Heights of Bean Plants (in Inches) | | | | |
|---|---|---|---|---|
| $2\frac{1}{4}$ | $2\frac{3}{4}$ | $3\frac{1}{4}$ | $1\frac{3}{4}$ | $1\frac{3}{4}$ |
| $1\frac{3}{4}$ | $3$ | $2\frac{1}{2}$ | $3\frac{1}{4}$ | $2\frac{1}{2}$ |
| $2$ | $2\frac{1}{4}$ | $3$ | $2\frac{1}{4}$ | $3$ |
| $2\frac{1}{2}$ | $3\frac{1}{4}$ | $1\frac{3}{4}$ | $2\frac{3}{4}$ | $2$ |

a.  Use the data to complete the line plot below.

Title: _____

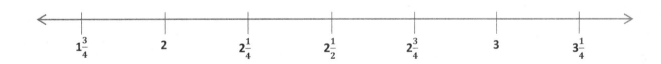

Label: _____    X =

©2015 Great Minds. eureka-math.org
G3-M6-SE-B4-1.3.1-01.2016

b.   How many bean plants are at least $2\frac{1}{4}$ inches tall?

c.   How many bean plants are taller than $2\frac{3}{4}$ inches?

d.   What is the most frequent measurement?  How many bean plants were plotted for this measurement?

e.   George says that most of the bean plants are at least 3 inches tall.  Is he right?  Explain your answer.

f.   Savannah was absent the day the class measured the heights of their bean plants.  When she returns, her plant measures $2\frac{2}{4}$ inches tall.  Can Savannah plot the height of her bean plant on the class line plot?  Why or why not?

**Lesson 7:**       Represent measurement data with line plots.                    EUREKA MATH

©2015 Great Minds. eureka-math.org
G3-M6-SE-B4-1.3.1-01.2016

Name _____   Date _____

Mrs. Felter's students build a model of their school's neighborhood out of blocks.  The students measure the heights of the buildings to the nearest $\frac{1}{4}$ inch and record the measurements as shown below.

| Heights of Buildings (in Inches) | | | | |
|---|---|---|---|---|
| $3\frac{1}{4}$ | $3\frac{3}{4}$ | $4\frac{1}{4}$ | $4\frac{1}{2}$ | $3\frac{1}{2}$ |
| 4 | 3 | $3\frac{3}{4}$ | 3 | $4\frac{1}{2}$ |
| 3 | $3\frac{1}{2}$ | $3\frac{3}{4}$ | $3\frac{1}{2}$ | 4 |
| $3\frac{1}{2}$ | $3\frac{1}{4}$ | $3\frac{1}{2}$ | 4 | $3\frac{3}{4}$ |
| 3 | $4\frac{1}{4}$ | 4 | $3\frac{1}{4}$ | 4 |

a.   Use the data to complete the line plot below.

Title: _____

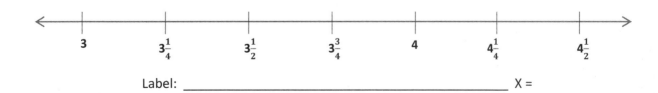

Label: _____ X =

EUREKA
MATH™

b.  How many buildings are $4\frac{1}{4}$ inches tall?

c.  How many buildings are less than $3\frac{1}{2}$ inches?

d.  How many buildings are in the class model?  How do you know?

e.  Brook says most buildings in the model are at least 4 inches tall.  Is she correct?  Explain your thinking.

| Straw Lengths (in Inches) | | | | |
| --- | --- | --- | --- | --- |
| 3 | 4 | $4\frac{1}{2}$ | $2\frac{3}{4}$ | $3\frac{3}{4}$ |
| $3\frac{3}{4}$ | $4\frac{1}{2}$ | $3\frac{1}{4}$ | 4 | $4\frac{3}{4}$ |
| $4\frac{1}{4}$ | 5 | 3 | $3\frac{1}{2}$ | $4\frac{1}{2}$ |
| $4\frac{3}{4}$ | 4 | $3\frac{1}{4}$ | 5 | $4\frac{1}{4}$ |

straw lengths

©2015 Great Minds. eureka-math.org
G3-M6-SE-B4-1.3.1-01.2016

This page intentionally left blank

Name _____ Date _____

Delilah stops under a silver maple tree and collects leaves.  At home, she measures the widths of the leaves to the nearest $\frac{1}{4}$ inch and records the measurements as shown below.

| Widths of Silver Maple Tree Leaves (in Inches) | | | | |
|---|---|---|---|---|
| $5\frac{3}{4}$ | $6$ | $6\frac{1}{4}$ | $6$ | $5\frac{3}{4}$ |
| $6\frac{1}{2}$ | $6\frac{1}{4}$ | $5\frac{1}{2}$ | $5\frac{3}{4}$ | $6$ |
| $6\frac{1}{4}$ | $6$ | $6$ | $6\frac{1}{2}$ | $6\frac{1}{4}$ |
| $6\frac{1}{2}$ | $5\frac{3}{4}$ | $6\frac{1}{4}$ | $6$ | $6\frac{3}{4}$ |
| $6$ | $6\frac{1}{4}$ | $6$ | $5\frac{3}{4}$ | $6\frac{1}{2}$ |

a.  Use the data to create a line plot below.

b.  Explain the steps you took to create the line plot.

c.  How many more leaves were 6 inches wide than $6\frac{1}{2}$ inches wide?

d.  Find the three most frequent measurements on the line plot.  What does this tell you about the typical width of a silver maple tree leaf?

Name _____     Date _____

Mrs. Leah's class uses what they learned about simple machines to build marshmallow launchers. They record the distances their marshmallows travel in the chart below.

| Distance Traveled (in Inches) | | | | |
|---|---|---|---|---|
| $48\frac{3}{4}$ | 49 | $49\frac{1}{4}$ | 50 | $49\frac{3}{4}$ |
| $49\frac{1}{2}$ | $48\frac{1}{4}$ | $49\frac{1}{2}$ | $48\frac{3}{4}$ | 49 |
| $49\frac{1}{4}$ | $49\frac{3}{4}$ | 48 | $49\frac{1}{4}$ | $48\frac{1}{4}$ |
| 49 | $48\frac{3}{4}$ | 49 | 49 | $48\frac{3}{4}$ |

a.   Use the data to create a line plot below.

b.  Explain the steps you took to create the line plot.

c.  How many more marshmallows traveled $48\frac{3}{4}$ inches than $48\frac{1}{4}$ inches?

d.  Find the three most frequent measurements on the line plot.  What does this tell you about the distance that most of the marshmallows traveled?

**Lesson 8:**   Represent measurement data with line plots.

EUREKA
MATH™

Mrs. Schaut measures the heights of the sunflower plants in her garden.  The measurements are shown in the chart below.

| Heights of Sunflower Plants (in Inches) | | | | |
|---|---|---|---|---|
| 61 | 63 | 62 | 61 | $62\frac{1}{2}$ |
| $61\frac{1}{2}$ | $61\frac{1}{2}$ | $61\frac{1}{2}$ | 62 | 60 |
| 64 | 62 | $60\frac{1}{2}$ | $63\frac{1}{2}$ | 61 |
| 63 | $62\frac{1}{2}$ | $62\frac{1}{2}$ | 64 | $62\frac{1}{2}$ |
| $62\frac{1}{2}$ | $63\frac{1}{2}$ | 63 | $62\frac{1}{2}$ | $63\frac{1}{2}$ |
| 62 | $62\frac{1}{2}$ | 62 | 63 | $60\frac{1}{2}$ |

heights of sunflower plants chart

©2015 Great Minds. eureka-math.org
G3-M6-SE-B4-1.3.1-01.2016

This page intentionally left blank

Name _____ Date _____

1.  Four children went apple picking.  The chart shows the number of apples the children picked.

| Name | Number of Apples Picked |
|---|---|
| Stewart | 16 |
| Roxanne | 24 |
| Trisha | 12 |
| Philip | 20 |
| **Total:** | 72 |

$$\begin{array}{r} 72 \\ -20 \\ \hline 52 \\ -12 \\ \hline 40 \\ -16 \\ \hline 24 \end{array}$$

a.  Find the number of apples Roxanne picked to complete the chart.

b.  Create a picture graph below using the data in the table.

**Apples Picked**

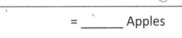
= _____ Apples

**Number of Apples Picked**

34, 32, 30, 28, 26, 24, 22, 20, 18, 16, 14, 12, 10, 8, 6, 4, 2

Stewart    Roxanne    Trisha    Philip

**Child**

2.  Use the chart or graph to answer the following questions.

    a.  How many more apples did Stewart and Roxanne pick than Philip and Trisha?

    b.  Trisha and Stewart combine their apples to make apples pies.  Each pie takes 7 apples.  How many
        pies can they make?

3.  Ms. Pacho's science class measured the lengths of blades of grass from their school field to the nearest
    $\frac{1}{4}$ inch.  The lengths are shown below.

| Lengths of Blades of Grass (in Inches) | | | | | |
|---|---|---|---|---|---|
| $2\frac{1}{4}$ | $2\frac{3}{4}$ | $3\frac{1}{4}$ | $3$ | $2\frac{1}{2}$ | $2\frac{3}{4}$ |
| $2\frac{3}{4}$ | $3\frac{3}{4}$ | $2$ | $2\frac{3}{4}$ | $3\frac{3}{4}$ | $3\frac{1}{4}$ |
| $3$ | $2\frac{1}{2}$ | $3\frac{1}{4}$ | $2\frac{1}{4}$ | $2\frac{3}{4}$ | $3$ |
| $3\frac{1}{4}$ | $2\frac{1}{4}$ | $3\frac{3}{4}$ | $3$ | $3\frac{1}{4}$ | $2\frac{3}{4}$ |

EUREKA
MATH

©2015 Great Minds. eureka-math.org
G3-M6-SE-B4-1.3.1-01.2016

a.  Make a line plot of the grass data.  Explain your choice of scale.

b.  How many blades of grass were measured?  Explain how you know.

c.  What was the length measured most frequently on the line plot?  How many blades of grass had this length?

d.  How many more blades of grass measured $2\frac{3}{4}$ inches than both $3\frac{3}{4}$ inches and 2 inches combined?

This page intentionally left blank

Name _____     Date _____

1. The table below shows the amount of money Danielle saves for four months.

| Month | Money Saved |
|---|---|
| January | $9 |
| February | $18 |
| March | $36 |
| April | $27 |

Create a picture graph below using the data in the table.

**Money Danielle Saves**

| | = _____ Dollars |
|---|---|

Money Saved

Month

2. Use the table or graph to answer the following questions.

   a. How much money does Danielle save in four months?

   b. How much more money does Danielle save in March and April than in January and February?

   c. Danielle combines her savings from March and April to buy books for her friends. Each book costs $9. How many books can she buy?

   d. Danielle earns $33 in June. She buys a necklace for $8 and a birthday present for her brother. She saves the $13 she has left. How much does the birthday present cost?

Lesson 9:     Analyze data to problem solve.

**EUREKA MATH**

©2015 Great Minds. eureka-math.org
G3-M6-SE-B4-1.3.1-01.2016

**Money Spent at the Fair**

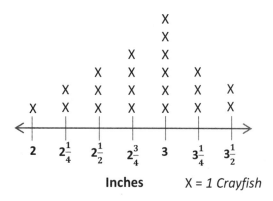

**Crayfish Lengths from Mr. Nye's Class**

bar graph and line plot

This page intentionally left blank

# Eureka Math
## Grade 3
## Module 7

Special thanks go to the Gordon A. Cain Center and to the Department of Mathematics at Louisiana State University for their support in the development of *Eureka Math*.

Name _____   Date _____

Lena's family visits Little Tree Apple Orchard.  Use the RDW process to solve the problems about Lena's visit to the orchard.  Use a letter to represent the unknown in each problem.

1.  The sign below shows information about hayrides at the orchard.

> **Hayrides**
>
> **Adult ticket . . . . . . . . $7**
>
> **Child ticket . . . . . . . . $4**
>
> **Leaves every 15 minutes starting at 11:00.**

a.  Lena's family buys 2 adult tickets and 2 child tickets for the hayride.  How much does it cost Lena's family to go on the hayride?

b.  Lena's mom pays for the tickets with $5 bills.  She receives $3 in change.  How many $5 bills does Lena's mom use to pay for the hayride?

c.  Lena's family wants to go on the fourth hayride of the day.  It's 11:38 now.  How many minutes do they have to wait for the fourth hayride?

2. Lena picked 17 apples, and her brother picked 19.  Lena's mom has a pie recipe that requires 9 apples.  How many pies can Mom make with the apples that Lena and her brother picked?

3. Lena's dad gives the cashier $30 to pay for 6 liters of apple cider.  The cashier gives him $6 in change.  How much does each liter of apple cider cost?

4. The apple orchard has 152 apple trees.  There are 88 trees with red apples.  The rest of the trees have green apples.  How many more trees have red apples than green apples?

**Lesson 1:**   Solve word problems in varied contexts using a letter to represent the unknown.

EUREKA MATH

Name _____   Date _____

Max's family takes the train to visit the city zoo.  Use the RDW process to solve the problems about Max's trip to the zoo.  Use a letter to represent the unknown in each problem.

1.   The sign below shows information about the train schedule into the city.

| Train Fare–One Way |
| --- |
| Adult.............................$8 |
| Child...........................$6 |
| Leaves every 15 minutes starting at 6:00 a.m. |

   a.   Max's family buys 2 adult tickets and 3 child tickets.  How much does it cost Max's family to take the train into the city?

   b.   Max's father pays for the tickets with $10 bills.  He receives $6 in change.  How many $10 bills does Max's father use to pay for the train tickets?

   c.   Max's family wants to take the fourth train of the day.  It's 6:38 a.m. now.  How many minutes do they have to wait for the fourth train?

Lesson 1:   Solve word problems in varied contexts using a letter to represent the unknown.

3

©2015 Great Minds. eureka-math.org
G3-M7-SE-B4-1.3.1-01.2016

2. At the city zoo, they see 17 young bats and 19 adult bats. The bats are placed equally into 4 areas. How many bats are in each area?

3. Max's father gives the cashier $20 to pay for 6 water bottles. The cashier gives him $8 in change. How much does each water bottle cost?

4. The zoo has 112 types of reptiles and amphibians in their exhibits. There are 72 types of reptiles, and the rest are amphibians. How many more types of reptiles are there than amphibians in the exhibits?

Lesson 1:   Solve word problems in varied contexts using a letter to represent the unknown.

©2015 Great Minds. eureka-math.org
G3-M7-SE-B4-1.3.1-01.2016

EUREKA
MATH

Date _____

...w process to solve.  Use a letter to represent the unknown in each problem.

120 tiles for an art project.  She has 56 tiles.  If tiles are sold in boxes of 8, how many more
...does Leanne need to buy?

2. Gwen pours 236 milliliters of water into Ravi's beaker.  Henry pours 189 milliliters of water into Ravi's
beaker.  Ravi's beaker now contains 800 milliliters of water.  How much water was in Ravi's beaker to
begin with?

3. Maude hung 3 pictures on her wall.  Each picture measures 8 inches by 10 inches.  What is the total area
of the wall covered by the pictures?

EUREKA
MATH™

Lesson 2:    Solve word problems in varied contexts using a letter to represent the
             unknown.

5

©2015 Great Minds. eureka-math.org
G3-M7-SE-B4-1.3.1-01.2016

4. Kami scored a total of 21 points during her basketball game. She made 6 two-point shots, and the rest were three-point shots. How many three-point shots did Kami make?

5. An orange weighs 198 grams. A kiwi weighs 85 grams less than the orange. What is the total weight of the fruit?

6. The total amount of rain that fell in New York City in two years was 282 centimeters. In the first year, 185 centimeters of rain fell. How many more centimeters of rain fell in the first year than in the second year?

EUREKA
MATH™

Name _____          Date _____

Use the RDW process to solve. Use a letter to represent the unknown in each problem.

1. A box containing 3 small bags of flour weighs 950 grams. Each bag of flour weighs 300 grams. How much does the empty box weigh?

2. Mr. Cullen needs 91 carpet squares. He has 49 carpet squares. If the squares are sold in boxes of 6, how many more boxes of carpet squares does Mr. Cullen need to buy?

3. Erica makes a banner using 4 sheets of paper. Each paper measures 9 inches by 10 inches. What is the total area of Erica's banner?

EUREKA MATH™

Lesson 2:    Solve word problems in varied contexts using a letter to represent the unknown.

7

©2015 Great Minds. eureka-math.org
G3-M7-SE-B4-1.3.1-01.2016

4. Monica scored 32 points for her team at the Science Bowl. She got 5 four-point questions correct, and the rest of her points came from answering three-point questions. How many three-point questions did she get correct?

5. Kim's black kitten weighs 175 grams. Her gray kitten weighs 43 grams less than the black kitten. What is the total weight of the two kittens?

6. Cassias and Javier's combined height is 267 centimeters. Cassias is 128 centimeters tall. How much taller is Javier than Cassias?

**Lesson 2:**   Solve word problems in varied contexts using a letter to represent the unknown.

EUREKA MATH

Name _____    Date _____

Use the RDW process to solve the problems below.  Use a letter to represent the unknown in each problem.  When you are finished, share your solutions with a partner.  Discuss and compare your strategies with your partner's strategies.

1.  Monica measures 91 milliliters of water into 9 tiny beakers.  She measures an equal amount of water into the first 8 beakers.  She pours the remaining water into the ninth beaker.  It measures 19 milliliters.  How many milliliters of water are in each of the first 8 beakers?

2.  Matthew and his dad put up 8 six-foot lengths of fence on Monday and 9 six-foot lengths on Tuesday.  What is the total length of the fence?

3.  The total weight of Laura's new pencils is 112 grams.  One pencil rolls off the scale.  Now the scale reads 105 grams.  What is the total weight of 7 new pencils?

Lesson 3:    Share and critique peer solution strategies to varied word problems.

9

©2015 Great Minds. eureka-math.org
G3-M7-SE-B4-1.3.1-01.2016

4.  Mrs. Ford's math class starts at 8:15.  They do 3 fluency activities that each last 4 minutes.  Just when they finish all of the fluency activities, the fire alarm goes off.  When they return to the room after the drill, it is 8:46.  How many minutes did the fire drill last?

5.  On Saturday, the baker bought a total of 150 pounds of flour in five-pound bags.  By Tuesday, he had 115 pounds of flour left.  How many five-pound bags of flour did the baker use?

6.  Fred cut an 84-centimeter rope into 2 parts and gave his sister 1 part.  Fred's part is 56 centimeters long. His sister cut her rope into 4 equal pieces.  How long is 1 of his sister's pieces of rope?

©2015 Great Minds. eureka-math.org
G3-M7-SE-B4-1.3.1-01.2016

EUREKA
MATH™

Name _____      Date _____

Use the RDW process to solve the problems below. Use a letter to represent the unknown in each problem.

1. Jerry pours 86 milliliters of water into 8 tiny beakers. He measures an equal amount of water into the first 7 beakers. He pours the remaining water into the eighth beaker. It measures 16 milliliters. How many milliliters of water are in each of the first 7 beakers?

2. Mr. Chavez's third graders go to gym class at 11:15. Students rotate through three activities for 8 minutes each. Lunch begins at 12:00. How many minutes are there between the end of gym activities and the beginning of lunch?

3. A box contains 100 pens. In each box there are 38 black pens and 42 blue pens. The rest are green pens. Mr. Cane buys 6 boxes of pens. How many green pens does he have in total?

4.  Greg has $56.  Tom has $17 more than Greg.  Jason has $8 less than Tom.

    a.  How much money does Jason have?

    b.  How much money do the 3 boys have in total?

5.  Laura cuts 64 inches of ribbon into two parts and gives her mom one part.  Laura's part is 28 inches long. Her mom cuts her ribbon into 6 equal pieces.  How long is one of her mom's pieces of ribbon?

©2015 Great Minds. eureka-math.org
G3-M7-SE-B4-1.3.1-01.2016

**Student A**

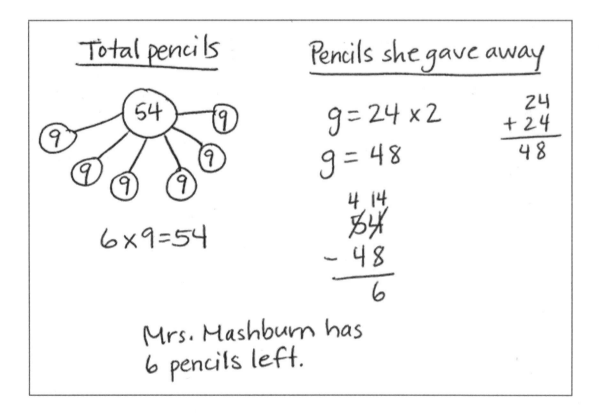

Total pencils

| 9 | 9 | 9 | 9 | 9 | 9 |

6 × 9 = 54

Pencils she gave away

24 × 2
(6 × 4) × 2
6 × (4 × 2)
6 × 8 = 48

$$\begin{array}{r} ^{4\ 14}\\ \cancel{54}\\ -\ 48\\ \hline 6 \end{array}$$

Mrs. Mashburn has 6
pencils left.

**Student B**

Total pencils

54
9 9 9 9 9 9

6 × 9 = 54

Pencils she gave away

g = 24 × 2
g = 48

$$\begin{array}{r} 24\\ +\ 24\\ \hline 48 \end{array}$$

$$\begin{array}{r} ^{4\ 14}\\ \cancel{54}\\ -\ 48\\ \hline 6 \end{array}$$

Mrs. Mashburn has
6 pencils left.

student work samples

Lesson 3:    Share and critique peer solution strategies to varied word problems.

13

©2015 Great Minds. eureka-math.org
G3-M7-SE-B4-1.3.1-01.2016

**Student C**

$$\begin{array}{r} \overset{4}{\cancel{5}}\overset{14}{\cancel{4}} \\ -48 \\ \hline 06 \end{array}$$

Mrs. Mashburn has 6 pencils left.

**Lesson 3:**   Share and critique peer solution strategies to varied word problems.

EUREKA MATH

©2015 Great Minds. eureka-math.org
G3-M7-SE-B4-1.3.1-01.2016

Name _____     Date _____

1. Cut out all the polygons (A–L) in the Template. Then, use the polygons to complete the following chart.

| Attribute | Write the letters of the polygons in this group. | Sketch 1 polygon from the group. |
|---|---|---|
| *Example:* **3 Sides** | Polygons: Y, Z | |
| **4 Sides** | Polygons: | |
| **At Least 1 Set of Parallel Sides** | Polygons: | |
| **2 Sets of Parallel Sides** | Polygons: | |
| **4 Right Angles** | Polygons: | |
| **4 Right Angles and 4 Equal Sides** | Polygons: | |

©2015 Great Minds. eureka-math.org
G3-M7-SE-B4-1.3.1-01.2016

2.  Write the letters of the polygons that are quadrilaterals.  Explain how you know these polygons are quadrilaterals.

3.  Sketch a polygon below from the group that has 2 sets of parallel sides.  Trace 1 pair of parallel sides red. Trace the other pair of parallel sides blue.  What makes parallel sides different from sides that are not parallel?

4.  Draw a diagonal line from one corner to the opposite corner of each polygon you drew in the chart using a straightedge.  What new polygon(s) did you make by drawing the diagonal lines?

EUREKA
MATH

Name _____    Date _____

1.  Complete the chart by answering true or false.

| Attribute | Polygon | True or False |
|---|---|---|
| *Example:*<br>**3 Sides** |  | True |
| **4 Sides** | | |
| **2 Sets of Parallel Sides** | | |
| **4 Right Angles** | | |
| **Quadrilateral** | | |

©2015 Great Minds. eureka-math.org
G3-M7-SE-B4-1.3.1-01.2016

2.  a.  Each quadrilateral below has at least 1 set of parallel sides.  Trace each set of parallel sides with a colored pencil.

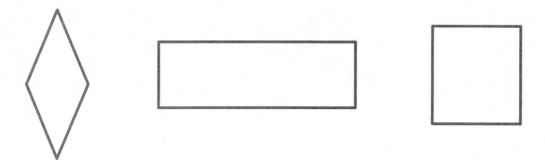

   b.  Using a straightedge, sketch a different quadrilateral with at least 1 set of parallel sides.

©2015 Great Minds. eureka-math.org
G3-M7-SE-B4-1.3.1-01.2016

EUREKA
MATH™

Name _____     Date _____

1.  Cut out all the polygons (M–X) in the Template.  Then, use the polygons to complete the following chart.

| Attribute | List polygons' letters for each group. | Sketch 1 polygon from the group. |
|---|---|---|
| *Example:* **3 Sides** | Polygons:  Y, Z |  |
| **All Sides Are Equal** | Polygons: | |
| **All Sides Are Not Equal** | Polygons: | |
| **At Least 1 Right Angle** | Polygons: | |
| **At Least 1 Set of Parallel Sides** | Polygons: | |

EUREKA
MATH™

©2015 Great Minds. eureka-math.org
G3-M7-SE-B4-1.3.1-01.2016

2. Compare Polygon M and Polygon X.  What is the same?  What is different?

3. Jenny says, "Polygon N, Polygon R, and Polygon S are all regular quadrilaterals!"  Is she correct?  Why or why not?

4. "I have six equal sides and six equal angles.  I have three sets of parallel lines.  I have no right angles."

   a.  Write the letter and the name of the polygon described above.

   b.  Estimate to draw the same type of polygon as in part (a), but with no equal sides.

Name _____   Date _____

1.  Match the polygons with their appropriate clouds.  A polygon can match to more than 1 cloud.

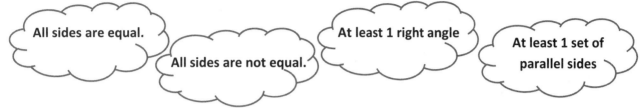

All sides are equal.

All sides are not equal.

At least 1 right angle

At least 1 set of parallel sides

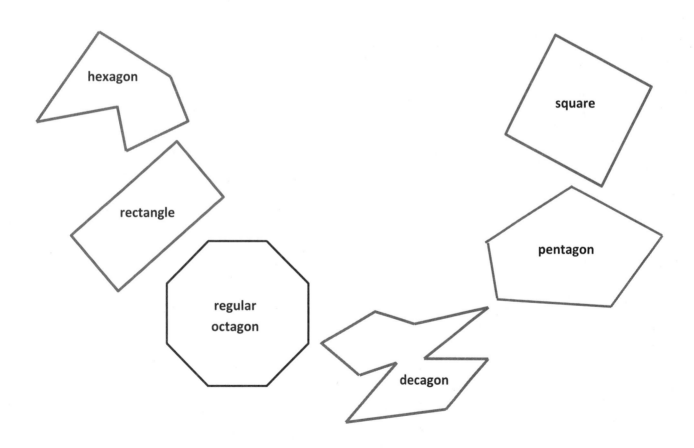

hexagon

square

rectangle

pentagon

regular octagon

decagon

2. The two polygons below are regular polygons.  How are these polygons the same?  How are they different?

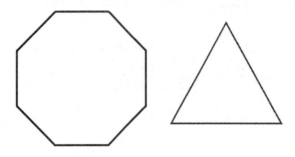

3. Lucia drew the polygons below.  Are any of the polygons she drew regular polygons?  Explain how you know.

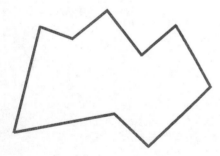  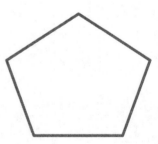

EUREKA
MATH™

Name _____     Date _____

Use a ruler and a right angle tool to help you draw the figures with the attributes given below.

1.  Draw a triangle with 1 right angle.

2.  Draw a quadrilateral with 4 right angles and sides that are all 2 inches long.

3.  Draw a quadrilateral with at least 1 set of parallel sides.  Trace the parallel sides green.

4. Draw a pentagon with at least 2 equal sides. Label the 2 equal side lengths of your shape.

5. Draw a hexagon with at least 2 equal sides. Label the 2 equal side lengths of your shape.

6. Sam says that he drew a polygon with 2 sides and 2 angles. Can Sam be correct? Use pictures to help you explain your answer.

EUREKA
MATH™

Name _____     Date _____

Use a ruler and a right angle tool to help you draw the figures with the given attributes below.

1.  Draw a triangle that has no right angles.

2.  Draw a quadrilateral that has at least 2 right angles.

3.  Draw a quadrilateral with 2 equal sides.  Label the 2 equal side lengths of your shape.

Lesson 6:   Draw polygons with specified attributes to solve problems.

25

©2015 Great Minds. eureka-math.org
G3-M7-SE-B4-1.3.1-01.2016

4.  Draw a hexagon with at least 2 equal sides.  Label the 2 equal side lengths of your shape.

5.  Draw a pentagon with at least 2 equal sides.  Label the 2 equal side lengths of your shape.

6.  Cristina describes her shape.  She says it has 3 equal sides that are each 4 centimeters in length.  It has no right angles.  Do your best to draw Cristina's shape, and label the side lengths.

©2015 Great Minds. eureka-math.org
G3-M7-SE-B4-1.3.1-01.2016

Name _____ Date _____

1. Use tetrominoes to create at least two different rectangles. Then, color the grid below to show how you created your rectangles. You may use the same tetromino more than once.

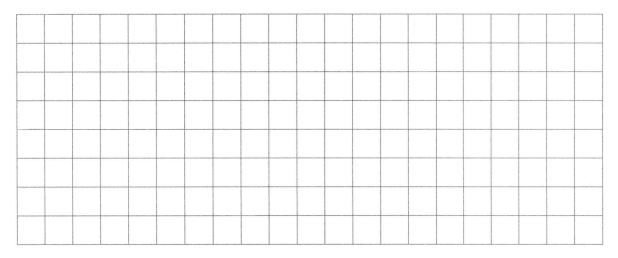

2. Use tetrominoes to create at least two squares, each with an area of 36 square units. Then, color the grid below to show how you created your squares. You may use the same tetromino more than once.

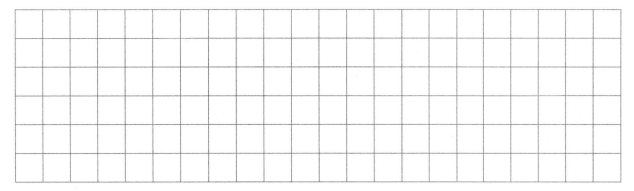

   a. Write an equation to show the area of a square above as the sum of the areas of the tetrominoes you used to make the square.

   b. Write an equation to show the area of a square above as the product of its side lengths.

Lesson 7:     Reason about composing and decomposing polygons using
              tetrominoes.

©2015 Great Minds. eureka-math.org
G3-M7-SE-B4-1.3.1-01.2016

27

3.  a.  Use tetrominoes to create at least two different rectangles, each with an area of 12 square units. Then, color the grid below to show how you created the rectangles.  You may use the same tetromino more than once.

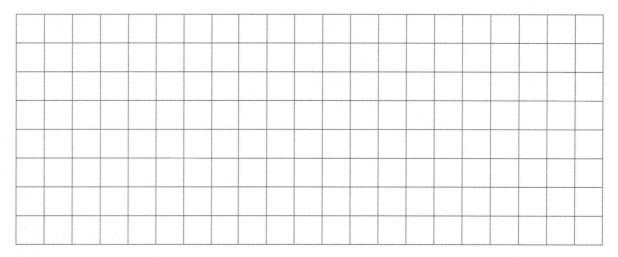

   b.  Explain how you know the area of each rectangle is 12 square units.

4.  Marco created a rectangle with tetrominoes and traced its outline in the space below.  Use tetrominoes to re-create it.  Estimate to draw lines inside the rectangle below to show how you re-created Marco's rectangle.

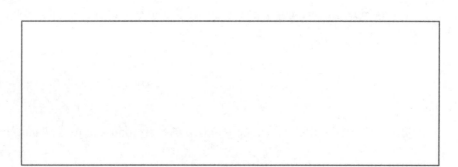

**Lesson 7:**      Reason about composing and decomposing polygons using
                            tetrominoes.

©2015 Great Minds. eureka-math.org
G3-M7-SE-B4-1.3.1-01.2016

EUREKA
MATH

Name _____     Date _____

1.  Color tetrominoes on the grid to create three different rectangles.  You may use the same tetromino more than once.

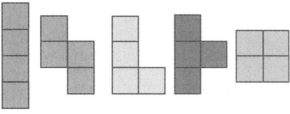

**Tetrominoes**

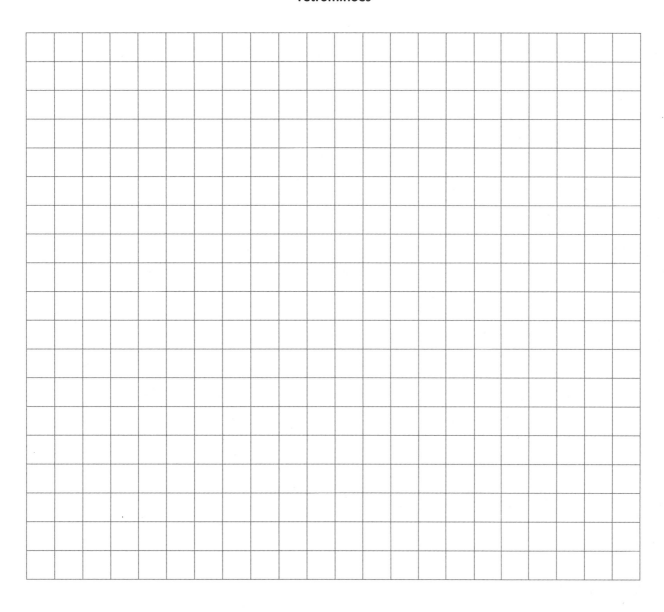

**Lesson 7:**    Reason about composing and decomposing polygons using
                 tetrominoes.

©2015 Great Minds. eureka-math.org
G3-M7-SE-B4-1.3.1-01.2016

29

2. Color tetrominoes on the grid below to:

   a. Create a square with an area of 16 square units.

   b. Create at least two different rectangles, each with an area of 24 square units.

   You may use the same tetromino more than once.

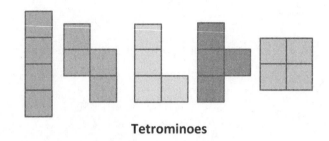

**Tetrominoes**

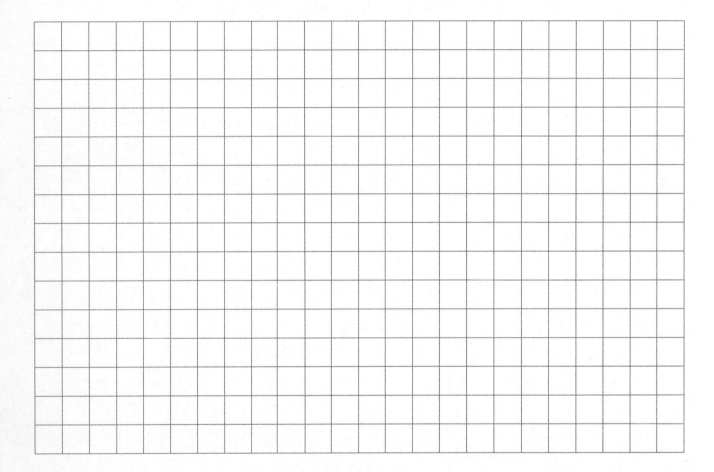

3. Explain how you know the rectangles you created in Problem 2(b) have the correct area.

Reason about composing and decomposing polygons using tetrominoes.

**EUREKA MATH**

Name _____     Date _____

1.  Fold and cut the square on the diagonal.  Draw and label your 2 new shapes below.

2.  Fold and cut one of the triangles in half.  Draw and label your 2 new shapes below.

3.  Fold twice, and cut your large triangle.  Draw and label your 2 new shapes below.

4.  Fold and cut your trapezoid in half.  Draw and label your 2 new shapes below.

Lesson 8:     Create a tangram puzzle and observe relationships among the shapes.

31

5. Fold and cut one of your trapezoids. Draw and label your 2 new shapes below.

6. Fold and cut your second trapezoid. Draw and label your 2 new shapes below.

7. Reconstruct the original square using the seven shapes.

   a. Draw lines inside the square below to show how the shapes go together to form the square. The first one has been done for you.

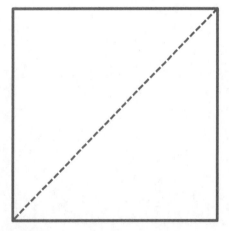

   b. Describe the process of forming the square. What was easy, and what was challenging?

EUREKA
MATH™

Name _____     Date _____

1.  Draw a line to divide the square below into 2 equal triangles.

2.  Draw a line to divide the triangle below into 2 equal, smaller triangles.

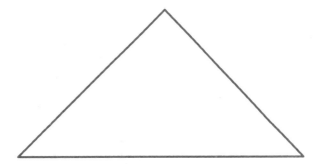

3.  Draw a line to divide the trapezoid below into 2 equal trapezoids.

4.  Draw 2 lines to divide the quadrilateral below into 4 equal triangles.

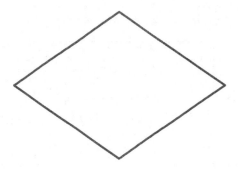

5.  Draw 4 lines to divide the square below into 8 equal triangles.

6.  Describe the steps you took to divide the square in Problem 5 into 8 equal triangles.

**Lesson 8:**      Create a tangram puzzle and observe relationships among the shapes.

EUREKA
MATH™

Name _____     Date _____

1. Use at least two tangram pieces to make and draw two of each of the following shapes. Draw lines to show where the tangram pieces meet.

   a. A rectangle that does not have all equal sides.

   b. A triangle.

   c. A parallelogram.

   d. A trapezoid.

2. Use your two smallest triangles to create a square, a parallelogram, and a triangle. Show how you created them below.

3. Create your own shape on a separate sheet of paper using all seven pieces. Describe its attributes below.

4. Trade your outline with a partner to see if you can re-create her shape using your tangram pieces. Reflect on your experience below. What was easy? What was challenging?

Name _____   Date _____

1. Use at least two tangram pieces to make and draw each of the following shapes. Draw lines to show where the tangram pieces meet.

    a. A triangle.

    b. A square.

    c. A parallelogram.

    d. A trapezoid.

©2015 Great Minds. eureka-math.org
G3-M7-SE-B4-1.3.1-01.2016

2.  Use your tangram pieces to create the cat below.  Draw lines to show where the tangram pieces meet.

3.  Use the five smallest tangram pieces to make a square.  Sketch your square below, and draw lines to show where the tangram pieces meet.

38

**Lesson 9:**     Reason about composing and decomposing polygons using tangrams.

EUREKA
MATH™

Name _____   Date _____

1.  Use a 2-inch square to answer the questions below.

    a.  Trace the square in the space below with a red crayon.

    b.  Trace the new shape you made with the square in the space below with a red crayon.

    c.  Which shape has a greater perimeter?  How do you know?

    d.  Color the inside of the shapes in Problem 1 (a) and (b) with a blue crayon.

Lesson 10:   Decompose quadrilaterals to understand perimeter as the boundary
             of a shape.

39

©2015 Great Minds. eureka-math.org
G3-M7-SE-B4-1.3.1-01.2016

e.  Which color represents the perimeters of the shapes?  How do you know?

f.  What does the other color represent?  How do you know?

g.  Which shape has a greater area?  How do you know?

2.  a.  Outline the perimeter of the shapes below with a red crayon.

 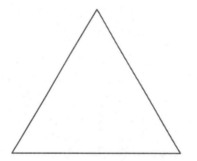 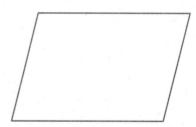

b.  Explain how you know you outlined the perimeters of the shapes above.

3.  Outline the perimeter of this piece of paper with a highlighter.

Lesson 10:   Decompose quadrilaterals to understand perimeter as the boundary
of a shape.

©2015 Great Minds. eureka-math.org
G3-M7-SE-B4-1.3.1-01.2016

EUREKA
MATH™

Name _____     Date _____

1.  Trace the perimeter of the shapes below.

   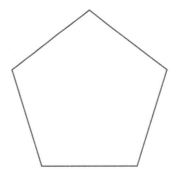

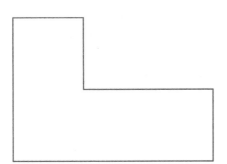   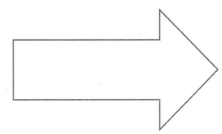

a.  Explain how you know you traced the perimeters of the shapes above.

b.  Explain how you could use a string to figure out which shape above has the greatest perimeter.

EUREKA
MATH™                    Lesson 10:       Decompose quadrilaterals to understand perimeter as the boundary          41
                                          of a shape.

©2015 Great Minds. eureka-math.org
G3-M7-SE-B4-1.3.1-01.2016

2. Draw a rectangle on the grid below.

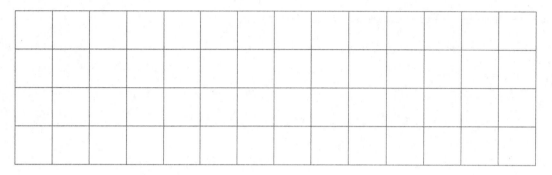

   a. Trace the perimeter of the rectangle.

   b. Shade the area of the rectangle.

   c. How is the perimeter of the rectangle different from the area of the rectangle?

3. Maya draws the shape shown below. Noah colors the inside of Maya's shape as shown. Noah says he colored the perimeter of Maya's shape. Maya says Noah colored the area of her shape. Who is right? Explain your answer.

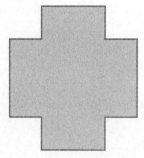

**Lesson 10:**    Decompose quadrilaterals to understand perimeter as the boundary
                          of a shape.

EUREKA
MATH™

Name _____    Date _____

1. Follow the directions below using the shape you created yesterday.

   a. Tessellate your shape on a blank piece of paper.

   b. Color your tessellation to create a pattern.

   c. Outline the perimeter of your tessellation with a highlighter.

   d. Use a string to measure the perimeter of your tessellation.

2. Compare the perimeter of your tessellation to a partner's.  Whose tessellation has a greater perimeter? How do you know?

3. How could you increase the perimeter of your tessellation?

4. How would overlapping your shape when you tessellated change the perimeter of your tessellation?

**Lesson 11:**    Tessellate to understand perimeter as the boundary of a shape. (Optional.)

43

©2015 Great Minds. eureka-math.org
G3-M7-SE-B4-1.3.1-01.2016

This page  intentionally left  blank

Name _____     Date _____

1.  Samson tessellates regular hexagons to make the shape below.

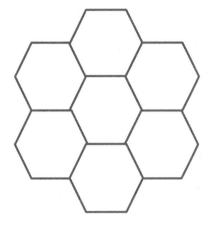

a.  Outline the perimeter of Samson's new shape with a highlighter.

b.  Explain how Samson could use a string to measure the perimeter of his new shape.

c.  How many sides does his new shape have?

d.  Shade in the area of his new shape with a colored pencil.

2.  Estimate to draw at least four copies of the given triangle to make a new shape, without gaps or overlaps.
    Outline the perimeter of your new shape with a highlighter.  Shade in the area with a colored pencil.

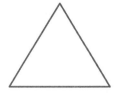

EUREKA
MATH™

**Lesson 11:**     Tessellate to understand perimeter as the boundary of a shape.
                   (Optional.)

45

©2015 Great Minds. eureka-math.org
G3-M7-SE-B4-1.3.1-01.2016

3. The marks on the strings below show the perimeters of Shyla's and Frank's shapes. Whose shape has a greater perimeter? How do you know?

Shyla's String:

Frank's String:

4. India and Theo use the same shape to create the tessellations shown below.

India's Tessellation                    Theo's Tessellation

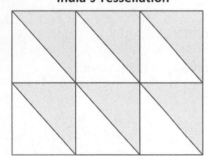                    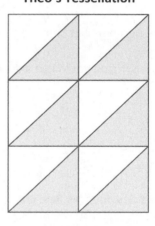

a. Estimate to draw the shape India and Theo used to make their tessellations.

b. Theo says both tessellations have the same perimeter. Do you think Theo is right? Why or why not?

Lesson 11: Tessellate to understand perimeter as the boundary of a shape.
(Optional.)

EUREKA MATH™

Name _____    Date _____

1. Measure and label the side lengths of the shapes below in centimeters. Then, find the perimeter of each shape.

a.

Perimeter = _____cm + _____cm + _____cm + _____cm

= _____ cm

b.

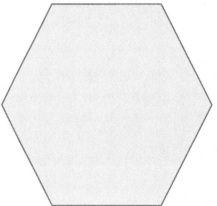

Perimeter = _____

= _____ cm

c.

Perimeter = _____

= _____ cm

d.

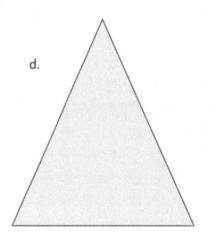

Perimeter = _____

= _____ cm

e.

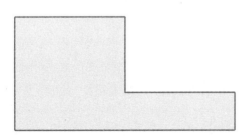

Perimeter = _____

= _____ cm

Lesson 12:    Measure side lengths in whole number units to determine the
perimeter of polygons.

47

©2015 Great Minds. eureka-math.org
G3-M7-SE-B4-1.3.1-01.2016

2. Carson draws two triangles to create the new shape shown below. Use a ruler to find the side lengths of Carson's shape in centimeters. Then, find the perimeter.

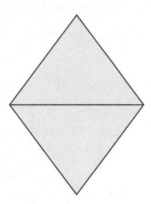

3. Hugh and Daisy draw the shapes shown below. Measure and label the side lengths in centimeters. Whose shape has a greater perimeter? How do you know?

**Hugh's Shape**

**Daisy's Shape**

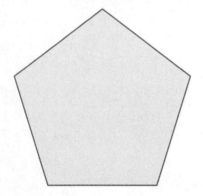

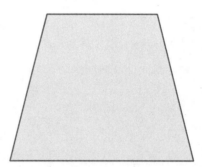

4. Andrea measures one side length of the square below and says she can find the perimeter with that measurement. Explain Andrea's thinking. Then, find the perimeter in centimeters.

**Lesson 12:**   Measure side lengths in whole number units to determine the perimeter of polygons.   **EUREKA MATH**

Name _____     Date _____

1. Measure and label the side lengths of the shapes below in centimeters.  Then, find the perimeter of each shape.

a.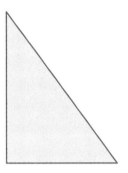

Perimeter = _____cm +_____cm +_____cm

= _____ cm

b.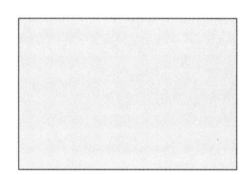

Perimeter = _____

= _____ cm

c.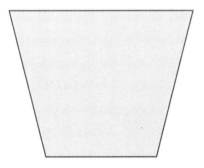

Perimeter = _____

= _____ cm

d.

Perimeter = _____

= _____ cm

e.

Perimeter = _____

= _____ cm

EUREKA
MATH

Lesson 12:      Measure side lengths in whole number units to determine the
                perimeter of polygons.

49

©2015 Great Minds. eureka-math.org
G3-M7-SE-B4-1.3.1-01.2016

2. Melinda draws two trapezoids to create the hexagon shown below. Use a ruler to find the side lengths of Melinda's hexagon in centimeters. Then, find the perimeter.

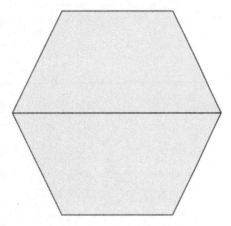

3. Victoria and Eric draw the shapes shown below. Eric says his shape has a greater perimeter because it has more sides than Victoria's shape. Is Eric right? Explain your answer.

**Victoria's Shape**          **Eric's Shape**

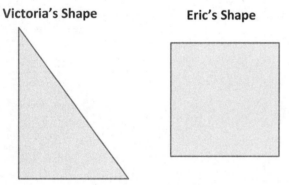

4. Jamal uses his ruler and a right angle tool to draw the rectangle shown below. He says the perimeter of his rectangle is 32 centimeters. Do you agree with Jamal? Why or why not?

EUREKA
MATH

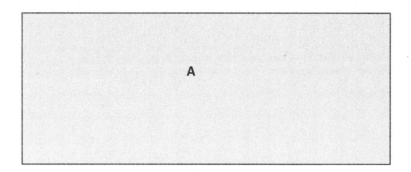

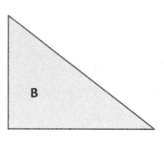

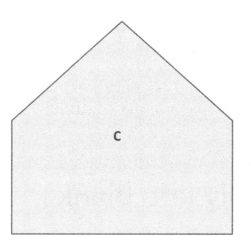

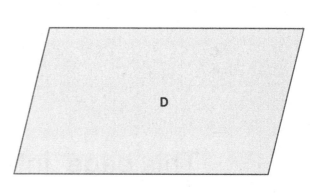

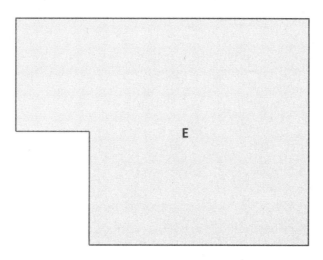

shapes

EUREKA MATH

**Lesson 12:**    Measure side lengths in whole number units to determine the
perimeter of polygons.

51

This page  intentionally left  blank

Name _____   Date _____

1.   Find the perimeter of the following shapes.

a.
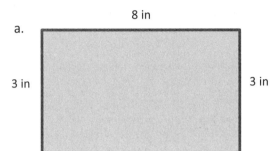

8 in

3 in                    3 in

8 in

P = 3 in + 8 in + 3 in + 8 in

= _____ in

b.
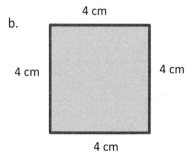

4 cm

4 cm                4 cm

4 cm

P = ____ cm + ____ cm + ____ cm + ____ cm

= _____ cm

c.
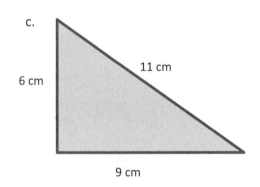

11 cm

6 cm

9 cm

P = ____ cm + ____ cm + ____ cm

= _____ cm

d.
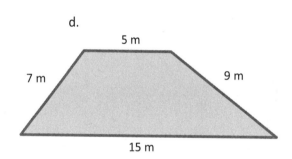

5 m

7 m                    9 m

15 m

P = ____ m + ____ m + ____ m + ____ m

= _____ m

e.
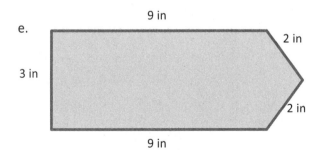

9 in

2 in

3 in

2 in

9 in

P = ____ in + ____ in + ____ in + ____ in + ____ in

= _____ in

EUREKA
MATH™

**Lesson 13:**      Explore perimeter as an attribute of plane figures and solve problems.

53

2. Alan's rectangular swimming pool is 10 meters long and 16 meters wide.  What is the perimeter?

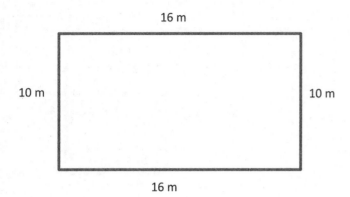

3. Lila measures each side of the shape below.

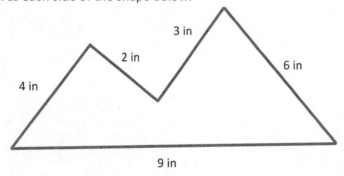

   a. What is the perimeter of the shape?

   b. Lila says the shape is a pentagon.  Is she correct?  Explain why or why not.

©2015 Great Minds. eureka-math.org
G3-M7-SE-B4-1.3.1-01.2016

Name _____     Date _____

1.  Find the perimeters of the shapes below.  Include the units in your equations.  Match the letter inside each shape to its perimeter to solve the riddle.  The first one has been done for you.

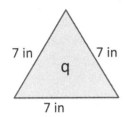

7 in        7 in
q
7 in

P = 7 in + 7 in + 7 in

P = 21 in

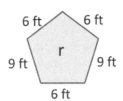

6 ft        6 ft
r
9 ft        9 ft
6 ft

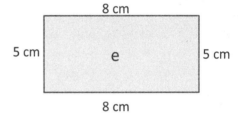

7 cm

5 cm        s        5 cm

7 cm

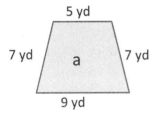

5 yd
7 yd        a        7 yd
9 yd

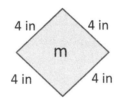

4 in        4 in
m
4 in        4 in

8 cm

5 cm        e        5 cm

8 cm

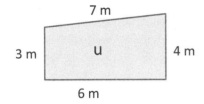

7 m
3 m        u        4 m
6 m

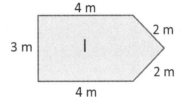

4 m
3 m        l        2 m
4 m        2 m

What kind of meals do math teachers eat?

_____  _____ _____ _____ _____ _____   _____ _____ _____ _____ _____ !

24       21      20      28      36      26        16      26      28      15      24

EUREKA
MATH™

2. Alicia's rectangular garden is 33 feet long and 47 feet wide.  What is the perimeter of Alicia's garden?

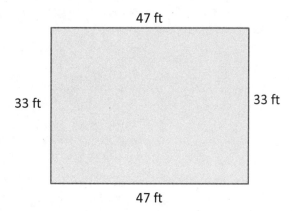

3. Jaques measured the side lengths of the shape below.

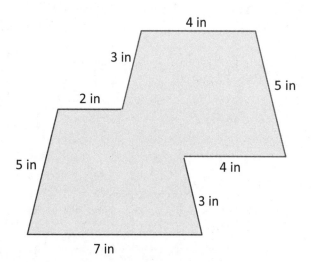

a.  Find the perimeter of Jaques's shape.

b.  Jaques says his shape is an octagon.  Is he right?  Why or why not?

EUREKA
MATH™

©2015 Great Minds. eureka-math.org
G3-M7-SE-B4-1.3.1-01.2016

Name _____     Date _____

1.  Label the unknown side lengths of the regular shapes below.  Then, find the perimeter of each shape.

a.

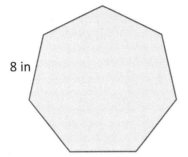

8 in

Perimeter = _____ in

b.

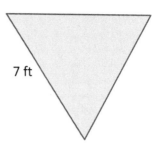

7 ft

Perimeter = _____ ft

c.

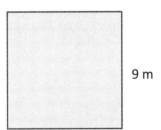

9 m

Perimeter = _____ m

d.

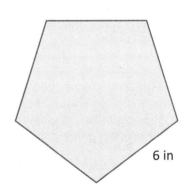

6 in

Perimeter = _____ in

2.  Label the unknown side lengths of the rectangle below.  Then, find the perimeter of the rectangle.

2 cm

7 cm

Perimeter = _____ cm

EUREKA
MATH™

Lesson 14:    Determine the perimeter of regular polygons and rectangles when
              whole number measurements are unknown.

57

©2015 Great Minds. eureka-math.org
G3-M7-SE-B4-1.3.1-01.2016

3. David draws a regular octagon and labels a side length as shown below.  Find the perimeter of David's octagon.

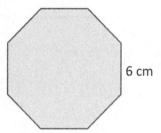
6 cm

4. Paige paints an 8-inch by 9-inch picture for her mom's birthday.  What is the total length of wood that Paige needs to make a frame for the picture?

5. Mr. Spooner draws a regular hexagon on the board.  One of the sides measures 4 centimeters.  Giles and Xander find the perimeter.  Their work is shown below.  Whose work is correct?  Explain your answer.

| Giles's Work | Xander's Work |
|---|---|
| Perimeter = 4 cm + 4 cm + 4 cm + 4 cm + 4 cm + 4 cm | Perimeter = 6 × 4 cm |
| Perimeter = 24 cm | Perimeter = 24 cm |

Determine the perimeter of regular polygons and rectangles when whole number measurements are unknown.

EUREKA
MATH

Name _____     Date _____

1.  Label the unknown side lengths of the regular shapes below.  Then, find the perimeter of each shape.

a.

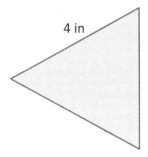

4 in

Perimeter = _____ in

b.

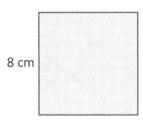

8 cm

Perimeter = _____ cm

c.

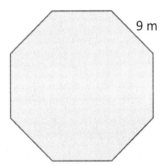

9 m

Perimeter = _____ m

d.

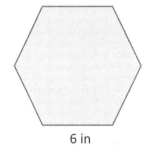

6 in

Perimeter = _____ in

2.  Label the unknown side lengths of the rectangle below.  Then, find the perimeter of the rectangle.

4 cm

9 cm     Perimeter = _____ cm

**EUREKA MATH**™

**Lesson 14:**   Determine the perimeter of regular polygons and rectangles when whole number measurements are unknown.

59

©2015 Great Minds. eureka-math.org
G3-M7-SE-B4-1.3.1-01.2016

3. Roxanne draws a regular pentagon and labels a side length as shown below. Find the perimeter of Roxanne's pentagon.

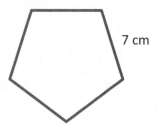 7 cm

4. Each side of a square field measures 24 meters. What is the perimeter of the field?

5. What is the perimeter of a rectangular sheet of paper that measures 8 inches by 11 inches?

Determine the perimeter of regular polygons and rectangles when whole number measurements are unknown.

EUREKA MATH™

Name _____    Date _____

1.  Mrs. Kozlow put a border around a 5-foot by 6-foot rectangular bulletin board.  How many feet of border did Mrs. Kozlow use?

2.  Jason built a model of the Pentagon for a social studies project.  He made each outside wall 33 centimeters long.  What is the perimeter of Jason's model pentagon?

3.  The Holmes family plants a rectangular 8-yard by 9-yard vegetable garden.  How many yards of fencing do they need to put a fence around the garden?

**Lesson 15:**    Solve word problems to determine perimeter with given side lengths.

61

©2015 Great Minds. eureka-math.org
G3-M7-SE-B4-1.3.1-01.2016

4. Marion paints a 5-pointed star on her bedroom wall. Each side of the star is 18 inches long. What is the perimeter of the star?

5. The soccer team jogs around the outside of the soccer field twice to warm up. The rectangular field measures 60 yards by 100 yards. What is the total number of yards the team jogs?

6. Troop 516 makes 3 triangular flags to carry at a parade. They sew ribbon around the outside edges of the flags. The flags' side lengths each measure 24 inches. How many inches of ribbon does the troop use?

**Lesson 15:**     Solve word problems to determine perimeter with given side lengths.

EUREKA
MATH™

Name _____     Date _____

1. Miguel glues a ribbon border around the edges of a 5-inch by 8-inch picture to create a frame. What is the total length of ribbon Miguel uses?

2. A building at Elmira College has a room shaped like a regular octagon. The length of each side of the room is 5 feet. What is the perimeter of this room?

3. Manny fences in a rectangular area for his dog to play in the backyard. The area measures 35 yards by 45 yards. What is the total length of fence that Manny uses?

4.  Tyler uses 6 craft sticks to make a hexagon.  Each craft stick is 6 inches long.  What is the perimeter of Tyler's hexagon?

5.  Francis made a rectangular path from her driveway to the porch.  The width of the path is 2 feet.  The length is 28 feet longer than the width.  What is the perimeter of the path?

6.  The gym teacher uses tape to mark a 4-square court on the gym floor as shown.  The outer square has side lengths of 16 feet.  What is the total length of tape the teacher uses to mark Square A?

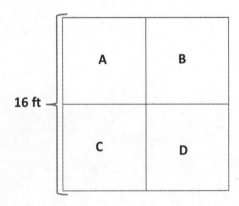

16 ft

A     B

C     D

Lesson 15:      Solve word problems to determine perimeter with given side lengths.

EUREKA MATH™

©2015 Great Minds. eureka-math.org
G3-M7-SE-B4-1.3.1-01.2016

Name _____   Date _____

1.  Find the perimeter of 10 circular objects to the nearest quarter inch using string.  Record the name and perimeter of each object in the chart below.

| Object | Perimeter (to the nearest quarter inch) |
|---|---|
|  |  |
|  |  |
|  |  |
|  |  |
|  |  |
|  |  |
|  |  |
|  |  |
|  |  |
|  |  |

a.  Explain the steps you used to find the perimeter of the circular objects in the chart above.

b.  Could the same process be used to find the perimeter of the shape below?  Why or why not?

Lesson 16:    Use string to measure the perimeter of various circles to the nearest quarter inch.

65

©2015 Great Minds. eureka-math.org
G3-M7-SE-B4-1.3.1-01.2016

2.  Can you find the perimeter of the shape below using just your ruler?  Explain your answer.

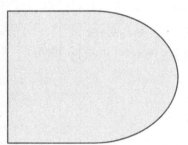

3.  Molly says the perimeter of the shape below is $6\frac{1}{4}$ inches.  Use your string to check her work.  Do you agree with her?  Why or why not?

4.  Is the process you used to find the perimeter of a circular object an efficient method to find the perimeter of a rectangle?  Why or why not?

**Lesson 16:**      Use string to measure the perimeter of various circles to the nearest quarter inch.

**EUREKA MATH**

Name _____     Date _____

1.  a.  Find the perimeter of 5 circular objects from home to the nearest quarter inch using string.  Record the name and perimeter of each object in the chart below.

| Object | Perimeter (to the nearest quarter inch) |
|---|---|
| Example:  Peanut Butter Jar Cap | $9\frac{1}{2}$ inches |
|  |  |
|  |  |
|  |  |
|  |  |
|  |  |

b.  Explain the steps you used to find the perimeter of the circular objects in the chart above.

2.   Use your string and ruler to find the perimeter of the two shapes below to the nearest quarter inch.

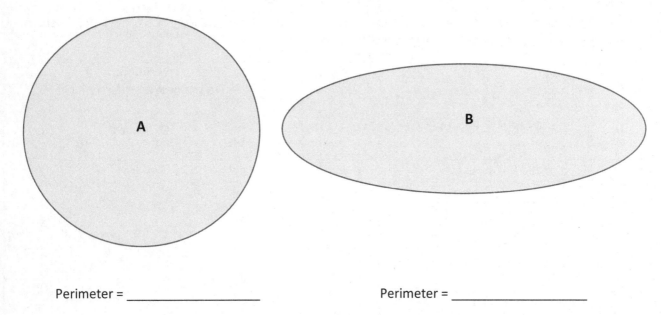

Perimeter = _____           Perimeter = _____

a.   Which shape has a greater perimeter?

b.   Find the difference between the two perimeters.

3.   Describe the steps you took to find the perimeter of the objects in Problem 2.  Would you use this method to find the perimeter of a square?  Explain why or why not.

68        **Lesson 16:**     Use string to measure the perimeter of various circles to the nearest
                          quarter inch.

                    ©2015 Great Minds. eureka-math.org
                    G3-M7-SE-B4-1.3.1-01.2016

EUREKA
MATH™

Name _____   Date _____

1. The shapes below are made up of rectangles. Label the unknown side lengths. Then, write and solve an equation to find the perimeter of each shape.

a.

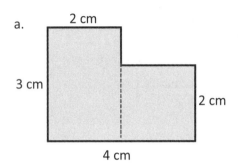

P =

b.

5 ft
2 ft
1 ft
2 ft          2 ft

P =

c.

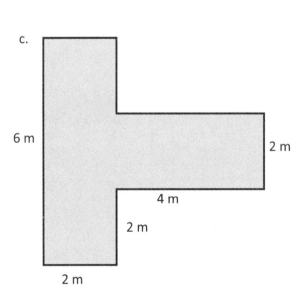

P =

d.

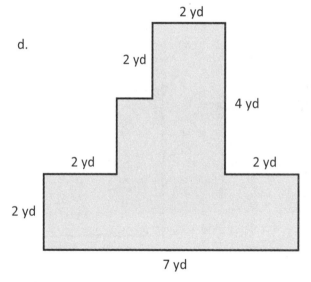

P =

EUREKA MATH™   **Lesson 17:**   Use all four operations to solve problems involving perimeter and unknown measurements.   **69**

©2015 Great Minds. eureka-math.org
G3-M7-SE-B4-1.3.1-01.2016

2. Nathan draws and labels the square and rectangle below. Find the perimeter of the new shape.

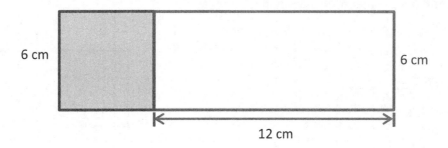

3. Label the unknown side lengths. Then, find the perimeter of the shaded rectangle.

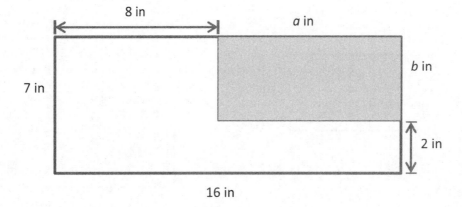

Use all four operations to solve problems involving perimeter and unknown measurements.

EUREKA
MATH™

Name _____    Date _____

1.  The shapes below are made up of rectangles.  Label the unknown side lengths.  Then, write and solve an equation to find the perimeter of each shape.

a.

7 m

2 m

9 m

4 m

P =

b.

8 cm

6 cm

5 cm

3 cm

4 cm

2 cm

2 cm

P =

c.

6 in

4 in          4 in

2 in

12 in

P =

d.

2 ft

3 ft

3 ft

7 ft

1 ft

8 ft

P =

EUREKA
MATH™

Lesson 17:    Use all four operations to solve problems involving perimeter and
unknown measurements.

71

2. Sari draws and labels the squares and rectangle below. Find the perimeter of the new shape.

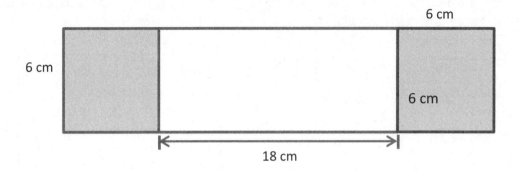

6 cm

6 cm

6 cm

18 cm

3. Label the unknown side lengths. Then, find the perimeter of the shaded rectangle.

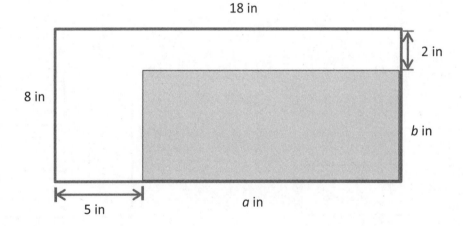

18 in

2 in

8 in

b in

5 in

a in

Lesson 17: Use all four operations to solve problems involving perimeter and unknown measurements.

©2015 Great Minds. eureka-math.org
G3-M7-SE-B4-1.3.1-01.2016

EUREKA
MATH

Name _____   Date _____

1. Use unit squares to build as many rectangles as you can with an area of 24 square units. Shade in squares on your grid paper to represent each rectangle that you made with an area of 24 square units.

   a. Estimate to draw and label the side lengths of each rectangle you built in Problem 1. Then, find the perimeter of each rectangle. One rectangle is done for you.

   **24 units**

   **1 unit**

   **P =** 24 units + 1 unit + 24 units + 1 unit = <u>50 units</u>

   b. The areas of the rectangles in part (a) above are all the same. What do you notice about the perimeters?

Lesson 18:  Construct rectangles from a given number of unit squares and
            determine the perimeters.

73

©2015 Great Minds. eureka-math.org
G3-M7-SE-B4-1.3.1-01.2016

EUREKA
MATH™

2. Use unit square tiles to build as many rectangles as you can with an area of 16 square units. Estimate to draw each rectangle below. Label the side lengths.

a. Find the perimeters of the rectangles you built.

b. What is the perimeter of the square? Explain how you found your answer.

3. Doug uses square unit tiles to build rectangles with an area of 15 square units. He draws the rectangles as shown below but forgets to label the side lengths. Doug says that Rectangle A has a greater perimeter than Rectangle B. Do you agree? Why or why not?

Rectangle A

Rectangle B

**Lesson 18:**     Construct rectangles from a given number of unit squares and
                                    determine the perimeters.

EUREKA
MATH

Name _____ Date _____

1.  Shade in squares on the grid below to create as many rectangles as you can with an area of 18 square centimeters.

2.  Find the perimeter of each rectangle in Problem 1 above.

EUREKA
MATH™

**Lesson 18:**   Construct rectangles from a given number of unit squares and determine the perimeters.

75

©2015 Great Minds. eureka-math.org
G3-M7-SE-B4-1.3.1-01.2016

3. Estimate to draw as many rectangles as you can with an area of 20 square centimeters. Label the side lengths of each rectangle.

   a. Which rectangle above has the greatest perimeter? How do you know just by looking at its shape?

   b. Which rectangle above has the smallest perimeter? How do you know just by looking at its shape?

**Lesson 18:**    Construct rectangles from a given number of unit squares and determine the perimeters.

EUREKA
MATH

grid paper

Lesson 18:    Construct rectangles from a given number of unit squares and
              determine the perimeters.

77

©2015 Great Minds. eureka-math.org
G3-M7-SE-B4-1.3.1-01.2016

This page intentionally left blank

Name _____   Date _____

1.  Use unit square tiles to make rectangles for each given number of unit squares.  Complete the charts to show how many rectangles you can make for each given number of unit squares.  The first one is done for you.  You might not use all the spaces in each chart.

Number of unit squares = **12**

Number of rectangles I made: <u>3</u>

| Width | Length |
|-------|--------|
| 1 | 12 |
| 2 | 6 |
| 3 | 4 |

Number of unit squares = **13**

Number of rectangles I made: ____

| Width | Length |
|-------|--------|
|  |  |
|  |  |
|  |  |

Number of unit squares = **14**

Number of rectangles I made: ____

| Width | Length |
|-------|--------|
|  |  |
|  |  |
|  |  |

Number of unit squares = **15**

Number of rectangles I made: ____

| Width | Length |
|-------|--------|
|  |  |
|  |  |
|  |  |

Number of unit squares = **16**

Number of rectangles I made: ____

| Width | Length |
|-------|--------|
|  |  |
|  |  |
|  |  |

Number of unit squares = **17**

Number of rectangles I made: ____

| Width | Length |
|-------|--------|
|  |  |
|  |  |
|  |  |

Number of unit squares = **18**

Number of rectangles I made: ____

| Width | Length |
|-------|--------|
|  |  |
|  |  |
|  |  |

Lesson 19:   Use a line plot to record the number of rectangles constructed from a given number of unit squares.

79

©2015 Great Minds. eureka-math.org
G3-M7-SE-B4-1.3.1-01.2016

2.  Create a line plot with the data you collected in Problem 1.

**Number of Rectangles Made with Unit Squares**

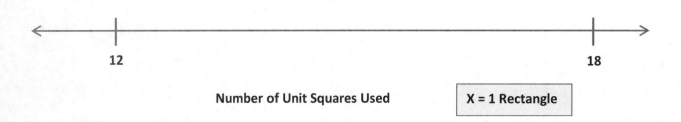

12                                                                              18

**Number of Unit Squares Used**          | X = 1 Rectangle |

3.  Which numbers of unit squares produce three rectangles?

4.  Why do some numbers of unit squares, such as 13, only produce one rectangle?

**Lesson 19:**     Use a line plot to record the number of rectangles constructed from a
                                   given number of unit squares.

EUREKA
MATH™

Name _____  Date _____

1.  Cut out the unit squares at the bottom of the page.  Then, use them to make rectangles for each given number of unit squares.  Complete the charts to show how many rectangles you can make for each given number of unit squares.  You might not use all the spaces in each chart.

Number of unit squares = **6**

Number of rectangles
I made: ____

| Width | Length |
|-------|--------|
|       |        |
|       |        |
|       |        |

Number of unit squares = **7**

Number of rectangles
I made: ____

| Width | Length |
|-------|--------|
|       |        |
|       |        |
|       |        |

Number of unit squares = **8**

Number of rectangles
I made: ____

| Width | Length |
|-------|--------|
|       |        |
|       |        |
|       |        |

Number of unit squares = **9**

Number of rectangles
I made: ____

| Width | Length |
|-------|--------|
|       |        |
|       |        |
|       |        |

Number of unit squares = **10**

Number of rectangles
I made: ____

| Width | Length |
|-------|--------|
|       |        |
|       |        |
|       |        |

Number of unit squares = **11**

Number of rectangles
I made: ____

| Width | Length |
|-------|--------|
|       |        |
|       |        |
|       |        |

✂ -----------------------------------------------------------------------------

Lesson 19:  Use a line plot to record the number of rectangles constructed from a given number of unit squares.

81

©2015 Great Minds. eureka-math.org
G3-M7-SE-B4-1.3.1-01.2016

This page intentionally left blank

2.  Create a line plot with the data you collected in Problem 1.

**Number of Rectangles Made with Unit Squares**

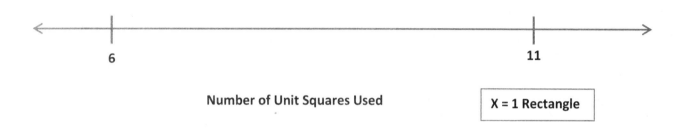

6                                                                11

**Number of Unit Squares Used**          | X = 1 Rectangle |

a.  Luke looks at the line plot and says that all odd numbers of unit squares produce only 1 rectangle.  Do you agree?  Why or why not?

b.  How many X's would you plot for 4 unit squares?  Explain how you know.

EUREKA MATH

Lesson 19:   Use a line plot to record the number of rectangles constructed from a given number of unit squares.

83

©2015 Great Minds. eureka-math.org
G3-M7-SE-B4-1.3.1-01.2016

This page intentionally left blank

Name _____     Date _____

1. Use your square unit tiles to build as many rectangles as you can with a perimeter of 12 units.

   a. Estimate to draw your rectangles below. Label the side lengths of each rectangle.

   b. Explain your strategy for finding rectangles with a perimeter of 12 units.

   c. Find the areas of all the rectangles in part (a) above.

   d. The perimeters of all the rectangles are the same. What do you notice about their areas?

**Lesson 20:**  Construct rectangles with a given perimeter using unit squares and
determine their areas.

85

©2015 Great Minds. eureka-math.org
G3-M7-SE-B4-1.3.1-01.2016

2. Use your square unit tiles to build as many rectangles as you can with a perimeter of 14 units.

    a. Estimate to draw your rectangles below. Label the side lengths of each rectangle.

    b. Find the areas of all the rectangles in part (a) above.

    c. Given a rectangle's perimeter, what other information do you need to know about the rectangle to find its area?

Construct rectangles with a given perimeter using unit squares and determine their areas.

EUREKA
MATH™

Name _____    Date _____

1.  Cut out the unit squares at the bottom of the page.  Then, use them to make as many rectangles as you can with a perimeter of 10 units.

    a.  Estimate to draw your rectangles below.  Label the side lengths of each rectangle.

    b.  Find the areas of the rectangles in part (a) above.

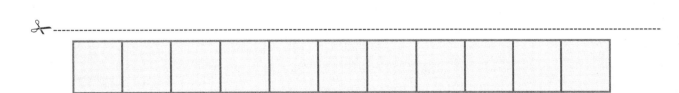

©2015 Great Minds. eureka-math.org
G3-M7-SE-B4-1.3.1-01.2016

This page  intentionally left  blank

2. Gino uses unit square tiles to make rectangles with a perimeter of 14 units. He draws his rectangles as shown below. Using square unit tiles, can Gino make another rectangle that has a perimeter of 14 units? Explain your answer.

6 units

1 unit

4 units

3 units

3. Katie draws a square that has a perimeter of 20 centimeters.

   a. Estimate to draw Katie's square below. Label the length and width of the square.

   b. Find the area of Katie's square.

   c. Estimate to draw a different rectangle that has the same perimeter as Katie's square.

   d. Which shape has a greater area, Katie's square or your rectangle?

EUREKA MATH

Lesson 20: Construct rectangles with a given perimeter using unit squares and determine their areas.

89

©2015 Great Minds. eureka-math.org
G3-M7-SE-B4-1.3.1-01.2016

Name _____  Date _____

Use the data you gathered from Problem Sets 20 and 21 to complete the charts to show how many rectangles you can create with a given perimeter.  You might not use all the spaces in the charts.

| Perimeter = 10 units | | |
|---|---|---|
| **Number of rectangles you made:** _____ | | |
| Width | Length | Area |
| 1 unit | 4 units | 4 square units |
| | | |
| | | |
| | | |

| Perimeter = 12 units | | |
|---|---|---|
| **Number of rectangles you made:** _____ | | |
| Width | Length | Area |
| | | |
| | | |
| | | |
| | | |

| Perimeter = 14 units | | |
|---|---|---|
| **Number of rectangles you made:** _____ | | |
| Width | Length | Area |
| | | |
| | | |
| | | |
| | | |

| Perimeter = 16 units | | |
|---|---|---|
| **Number of rectangles you made:** _____ | | |
| Width | Length | Area |
| | | |
| | | |
| | | |
| | | |

| Perimeter = 18 units | | |
|---|---|---|
| **Number of rectangles you made:** _____ | | |
| Width | Length | Area |
| | | |
| | | |
| | | |
| | | |
| | | |

| Perimeter = 20 units | | |
|---|---|---|
| **Number of rectangles you made:** _____ | | |
| Width | Length | Area |
| | | |
| | | |
| | | |
| | | |
| | | |

**Lesson 20:**    Construct rectangles with a given perimeter using unit squares and determine their areas.

EUREKA MATH™

©2015 Great Minds. eureka-math.org
G3-M7-SE-B4-1.3.1-01.2016

Name _____     Date _____

1.  On your centimeter grid paper, shade and label as many rectangles as you can with a perimeter of 16 centimeters.

    a.  Sketch the rectangles below, and label the side lengths.

    b.  Find the area of each rectangle you drew above.

2.  On your centimeter grid paper, shade and label as many rectangles as you can with a perimeter of 18 centimeters.

    a.  Sketch the rectangles below, and label the side lengths.

    b.  Find the area of each rectangle you drew above.

Lesson 21:     Construct rectangles with a given perimeter using unit squares and          91
               determine their areas.

©2015 Great Minds. eureka-math.org
G3-M7-SE-B4-1.3.1-01.2016

3. Use centimeter grid paper to shade in as many rectangles as you can with the given perimeters.

   a. Use the charts below to show how many rectangles you shaded for each given perimeter. You might not use all the spaces in the charts.

| Perimeter = 10 cm | | |
|---|---|---|
| Number of rectangles I made: ____ | | |
| Width | Length | Area |
| 1 cm | 4 cm | 4 square cm |
| | | |
| | | |
| | | |
| | | |

| Perimeter = 20 cm | | |
|---|---|---|
| Number of rectangles I made: ____ | | |
| Width | Length | Area |
| 1 cm | 9 cm | 9 square cm |
| | | |
| | | |
| | | |
| | | |

   b. Did you make a square with either of the given perimeters? How do you know?

4. Macy and Gavin both draw rectangles with perimeters of 16 centimeters. Use words and pictures to explain how it is possible for Macy's and Gavin's rectangles to have the same perimeters but different areas.

Lesson 21:    Construct rectangles with a given perimeter using unit squares and determine their areas.

EUREKA MATH

Name _____      Date _____

1. Margo finds as many rectangles as she can with a perimeter of 14 centimeters.

    a. Shade Margo's rectangles on the grid below. Label the length and width of each rectangle.

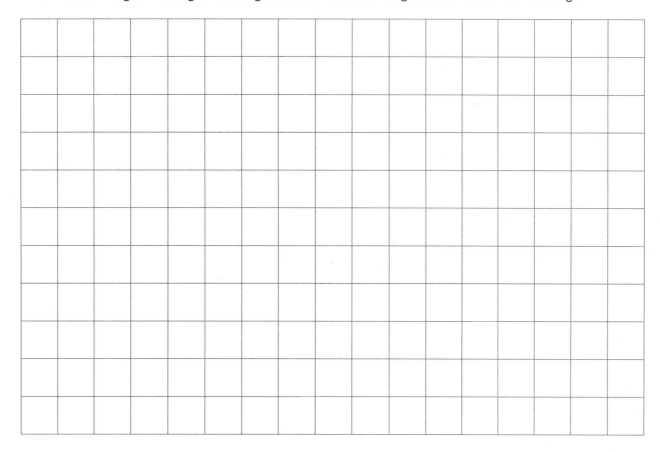

    b. Find the areas of the rectangles in part (a) above.

    c. The perimeters of the rectangles are the same. What do you notice about the areas?

**EUREKA MATH™**     **Lesson 21:**    Construct rectangles with a given perimeter using unit squares and determine their areas.       **93**

©2015 Great Minds. eureka-math.org
G3-M7-SE-B4-1.3.1-01.2016

2. Tanner uses unit squares to build rectangles that have a perimeter of 18 units.  He creates the chart below to record his findings.

   a.  Complete Tanner's chart.  You might not use all the spaces in the chart.

   | Perimeter = 18 units | | |
   |---|---|---|
   | Number of rectangles I made: _____ | | |
   | Width | Length | Area |
   | 1 unit | 8 units | 8 square units |
   | | | |
   | | | |
   | | | |
   | | | |

   b.  Explain how you found the widths and lengths in the chart above.

3. Jason and Dina both draw rectangles with perimeters of 12 centimeters, but their rectangles have different areas.  Explain with words, pictures, and numbers how this is possible.

Lesson 21:      Construct rectangles with a given perimeter using unit squares and
                          determine their areas.

©2015 Great Minds. eureka-math.org
G3-M7-SE-B4-1.3.1-01.2016

EUREKA
MATH

centimeter grid paper

**Lesson 21:**    Construct rectangles with a given perimeter using unit squares and
determine their areas.

95

©2015 Great Minds. eureka-math.org
G3-M7-SE-B4-1.3.1-01.2016

This page intentionally left blank

Name _____    Date _____

Use the data you gathered from Problem Sets 20 and 21 to complete the charts to show how many rectangles you can create with a given perimeter.  You might not use all the spaces in the charts.

| Perimeter = 10 units |  |  |
| --- | --- | --- |
| Number of rectangles you made: _____ |  |  |
| Width | Length | Area |
| 1 unit | 4 units | 4 square units |
|  |  |  |
|  |  |  |
|  |  |  |

| Perimeter = 12 units |  |  |
| --- | --- | --- |
| Number of rectangles you made: _____ |  |  |
| Width | Length | Area |
|  |  |  |
|  |  |  |
|  |  |  |
|  |  |  |

| Perimeter = 14 units |  |  |
| --- | --- | --- |
| Number of rectangles you made: _____ |  |  |
| Width | Length | Area |
|  |  |  |
|  |  |  |
|  |  |  |
|  |  |  |

| Perimeter = 16 units |  |  |
| --- | --- | --- |
| Number of rectangles you made: _____ |  |  |
| Width | Length | Area |
|  |  |  |
|  |  |  |
|  |  |  |
|  |  |  |

| Perimeter = 18 units |  |  |
| --- | --- | --- |
| Number of rectangles you made: _____ |  |  |
| Width | Length | Area |
|  |  |  |
|  |  |  |
|  |  |  |
|  |  |  |
|  |  |  |

| Perimeter = 20 units |  |  |
| --- | --- | --- |
| Number of rectangles you made: _____ |  |  |
| Width | Length | Area |
|  |  |  |
|  |  |  |
|  |  |  |
|  |  |  |
|  |  |  |

**Lesson 21:**  Construct rectangles with a given perimeter using unit squares and determine their areas.

97

©2015 Great Minds. eureka-math.org
G3-M7-SE-B4-1.3.1-01.2016

This page intentionally left blank

Name _____ Date _____

1. Use the data you gathered from your Problem Sets to create a line plot for the number of rectangles you created with each given perimeter.

**Number of Rectangles Made with a Given Perimeter**

**Perimeter Measurements in Units**

| X = 1 Rectangle |
| --- |

2. Why are all of the perimeter measurements even? Do all rectangles have an even perimeter?

EUREKA MATH

**Lesson 22:** Use a line plot to record the number of rectangles constructed in Lessons 20 and 21.

99

©2015 Great Minds. eureka-math.org
G3-M7-SE-B4-1.3.1-01.2016

3. Compare the two line plots we created.  Is there any reason to think that knowing only the area of a rectangle would help you to figure out its perimeter or knowing only the perimeter of a rectangle would help you figure out its area?

4. Sumi uses unit square tiles to build 3 rectangles that have an area of 32 square units.  Does knowing this help her find the number of rectangles she can build for a perimeter of 32 units?  Why or why not?

5. George draws 3 rectangles that have a perimeter of 14 centimeters.  Alicia tells George that there are more than 3 rectangles that have a perimeter of 14 centimeters.  Explain why Alicia is correct.

Use a line plot to record the number of rectangles constructed in
             Lessons 20 and 21.

EUREKA
MATH™

Name _____   Date _____

1.  The following line plot shows the number of rectangles a student made using square unit tiles. Use the line plot to answer the questions below.

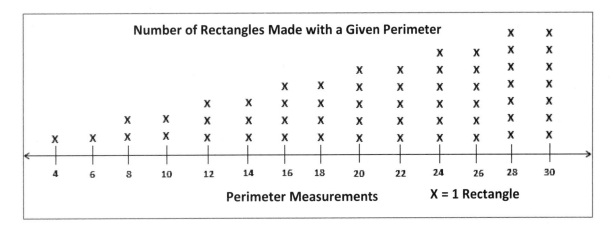

a.  Why are all of the perimeter measurements even? Do all rectangles have even perimeters?

b.  Explain the pattern in the line plot. What types of side lengths make this pattern possible?

c.  How many X's would you draw for a perimeter of 32? Explain how you know.

EUREKA
MATH™

Lesson 22:   Use a line plot to record the number of rectangles constructed in
             Lessons 20 and 21.

101

©2015 Great Minds. eureka-math.org
G3-M7-SE-B4-1.3.1-01.2016

2. Luis uses square inch tiles to build a rectangle with a perimeter of 24 inches. Does knowing this help him find the number of rectangles he can build with an area of 24 square inches? Why or why not?

3. Esperanza makes a rectangle with a piece of string. She says the perimeter of her rectangle is 33 centimeters. Explain how it's possible for her rectangle to have an odd perimeter.

**Lesson 22:** Use a line plot to record the number of rectangles constructed in Lessons 20 and 21.

©2015 Great Minds. eureka-math.org
G3-M7-SE-B4-1.3.1-01.2016

EUREKA
MATH

Name _____    Date _____

1.  Gale makes a miniature stop sign, a regular octagon, with a perimeter of 48 centimeters for the town he built with blocks.  What is the length of each side of the stop sign?

2.  Travis bends wire to make rectangles.  Each rectangle measures 34 inches by 12 inches.  What is the total length of the wire needed for two rectangles?

3.  The perimeter of a rectangular bathroom is 32 feet.  The width of the room is 8 feet.  What is the length of the room?

EUREKA
MATH™

Lesson 23:    Solve a variety of word problems with perimeter.

103

©2015 Great Minds. eureka-math.org
G3-M7-SE-B4-1.3.1-01.2016

4. Raj uses 6-inch square tiles to make a rectangle, as shown below. What is the perimeter of the rectangle in inches?

**6 in**

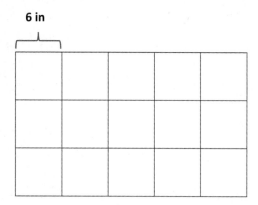

5. Mischa makes a 4-foot by 6-foot rectangular banner. She puts ribbon around the outside edges. The ribbon costs $2 per foot. What is the total cost of the ribbon?

6. Colton buys a roll of wire fencing that is 120 yards long. He uses it to fence in his 18-yard by 24-yard rectangular garden. Will Colton have enough wire fencing left over to fence in a 6-yard by 8-yard rectangular play space for his pet rabbit?

©2015 Great Minds. eureka-math.org
G3-M7-SE-B4-1.3.1-01.2016

Name _____   Date _____

1.  Rosie draws a square with a perimeter of 36 inches.  What are the side lengths of the square?

2.  Judith uses craft sticks to make two 24-inch by 12-inch rectangles.  What is the total perimeter of the 2 rectangles?

3.  An architect draws a square and a rectangle, as shown below, to represent a house that has a garage. What is the total perimeter of the house with its attached garage?

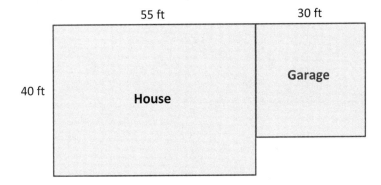

©2015 Great Minds. eureka-math.org
G3-M7-SE-B4-1.3.1-01.2016

4. Manny draws 3 regular pentagons to create the shape shown below. The perimeter of 1 of the pentagons is 45 inches. What is the perimeter of Manny's new shape?

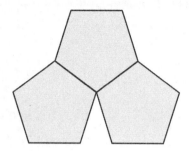

5. Johnny uses 2-inch square tiles to make a square, as shown below. What is the perimeter of Johnny's square?

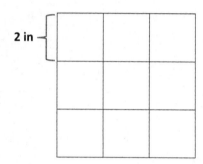

6. Lisa tapes three 7-inch by 9-inch pieces of construction paper together to make a happy birthday sign for her mom. She uses a piece of ribbon that is 144 inches long to make a border around the outside edges of the sign. How much ribbon is leftover?

**9 in**

**7 in**

Lesson 23:     Solve a variety of word problems with perimeter.

Name _____     Date _____

Use the given perimeters in the chart below to choose the widths and lengths of your robot's rectangular body parts.  Write the widths and lengths in the chart below.  Use the blank rows if you want to add extra rectangular body parts to your robot.

| Letter | Body Part | Perimeter | Width and Length |
|---|---|---|---|
| A | arm | 14 cm | _____ cm by _____ cm |
| B | arm | 14 cm | _____ cm by _____ cm |
| C | leg | 18 cm | _____ cm by _____ cm |
| D | leg | 18 cm | _____ cm by _____ cm |
| E | body | Double the perimeter of one arm = _____ cm | _____ cm by _____ cm |
| F | head | 16 cm | _____ cm by _____ cm |
| G | neck | Half the perimeter of the head = _____ cm | _____ cm by _____ cm |
| H | | | _____ cm by _____ cm |
| I | | | _____ cm by _____ cm |
| My robot has 7 to 9 rectangular body parts.  Number of body parts: _____ | | | |

     Lesson 24:    Use rectangles to draw a robot with specified perimeter measurements, and reason about the different areas that may be produced.        107

©2015 Great Minds. eureka-math.org
G3-M7-SE-B4-1.3.1-01.2016

Use the information in the chart below to plan an environment for your robot. Write the width and length for each rectangular item. Use the blank rows if you want to add extra circular or rectangular items to your robot's environment.

| Letter | Item | Shape | Perimeter | Width and Length |
|--------|------|-------|-----------|------------------|
| J | sun | circle | about 25 cm | |
| K | house | rectangle | 82 cm | _____ cm by _____ cm |
| L | tree top | circle | about 30 cm | |
| M | tree trunk | rectangle | 30 cm | _____ cm by _____ cm |
| N | tree top | circle | about 20 cm | |
| O | tree trunk | rectangle | 20 cm | _____ cm by _____ cm |
| P | | | | |
| Q | | | | |

My robot's environment has 6 to 8 items. Number of items: _____

Lesson 24:   Use rectangles to draw a robot with specified perimeter measurements, and reason about the different areas that may be produced.

©2015 Great Minds. eureka-math.org
G3-M7-SE-B4-1.3.1-01.2016

Name _____     Date _____

1. Brian draws a square with a perimeter of 24 inches. What is the width and length of the square?

2. A rectangle has a perimeter of 18 centimeters.

   a. Estimate to draw as many different rectangles as you can that have a perimeter of 18 centimeters. Label the width and length of each rectangle.

   b. How many different rectangles did you find?

   c. Explain the strategy you used to find the rectangles.

**Lesson 24:**    Use rectangles to draw a robot with specified perimeter measurements, and reason about the different areas that may be produced.

©2015 Great Minds. eureka-math.org
G3-M7-SE-B4-1.3.1-01.2016

109

3.  The chart below shows the perimeters of three rectangles.

    a.  Write possible widths and lengths for each given perimeter.

| Rectangle | Perimeter | Width and Length |
|-----------|-----------|------------------|
| A | 6 cm | _____ cm by _____ cm |
| B | 10 cm | _____ cm by _____ cm |
| C | 14 cm | _____ cm by _____ cm |

    b.  Double the perimeters of the rectangles in part (a).  Then, find possible widths and lengths.

| Rectangle | Perimeter | Width and Length |
|-----------|-----------|------------------|
| A | 12 cm | _____ cm by _____ cm |
| B |  | _____ cm by _____ cm |
| C |  | _____ cm by _____ cm |

Lesson 24:     Use rectangles to draw a robot with specified perimeter measurements, and reason about the different areas that may be produced.

©2015 Great Minds. eureka-math.org
G3-M7-SE-B4-1.3.1-01.2016

EUREKA
MATH™

Name _____    Date _____

Draw a picture of your robot in its environment in the space below.  Label the widths, lengths, and perimeters of all rectangles.  Label the perimeters of all circular shapes.

**Lesson 25:**    Use rectangles to draw a robot with specified perimeter
measurements, and reason about the different areas that may be
produced.

©2015 Great Minds. eureka-math.org
G3-M7-SE-B4-1.3.1-01.2016

111

This page intentionally left blank

Name _____    Date _____

The robot below is made of rectangles. The side lengths of each rectangle are labeled. Find the perimeter of each rectangle, and record it in the table on the next page.

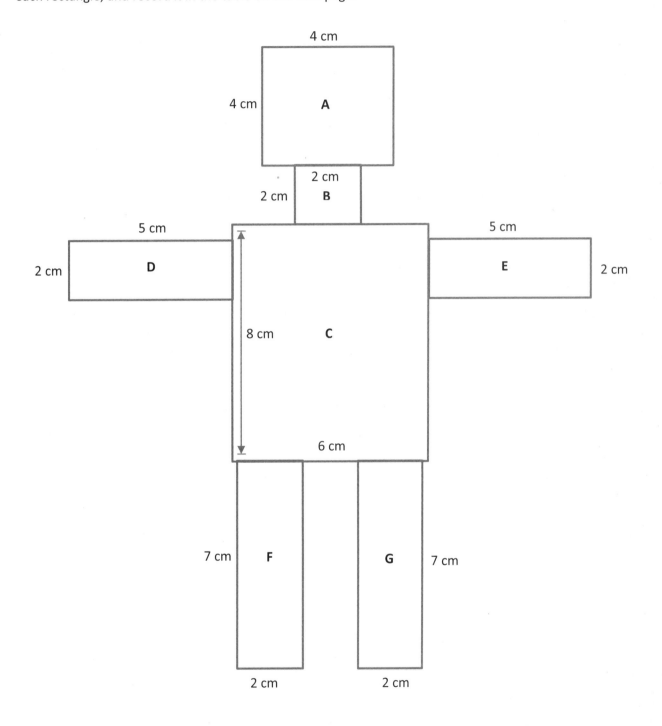

**Lesson 25:**    Use rectangles to draw a robot with specified perimeter measurements, and reason about the different areas that may be produced.

©2015 Great Minds. eureka-math.org
G3-M7-SE-B4-1.3.1-01.2016

113

| Rectangle | Perimeter |
|-----------|-----------|
| A | P = 4 × 4 cm<br>P = 16 cm |
| B | |
| C | |
| D | |
| E | |
| F | |
| G | |

**Lesson 25:** Use rectangles to draw a robot with specified perimeter measurements, and reason about the different areas that may be produced.

EUREKA MATH

Name _____ Date _____

1. Collect the area measurements of your classmates' **robot bodies**. Make a line plot using everyone's area measurements.

**Areas of Robot Bodies**

←————————————————————————————————————→

**Area Measurements of the Robot's Body in
Square Centimeters**

| X = 1 Robot Body |
|---|

a. How many different measurements are on the line plot? Why are the measurements different?

b. What does this tell you about the relationship between area and perimeter?

**Lesson 26:** Use rectangles to draw a robot with specified perimeter measurements, and reason about the different areas that may be produced.

115

©2015 Great Minds. eureka-math.org
G3-M7-SE-B4-1.3.1-01.2016

2. Measure and calculate the perimeter of your construction paper in inches. Show your work below.

3. Sketch and label two shapes with the same perimeter from the robot's environment. What do you notice about the way they look?

4. Write two or three sentences describing your robot and the environment in which it lives.

Lesson 26: Use rectangles to draw a robot with specified perimeter measurements, and reason about the different areas that may be produced.

©2015 Great Minds. eureka-math.org
G3-M7-SE-B4-1.3.1-01.2016

EUREKA
MATH™

Name _____     Date _____

1.  Use Rectangles A and B to answer the questions below.

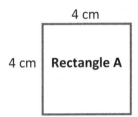

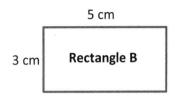

a.  What is the perimeter of Rectangle A?

b.  What is the perimeter of Rectangle B?

c.  What is the area of Rectangle A?

d.  What is the area of Rectangle B?

e.  Use your answers to parts (a–d) to help you explain the relationship between area and perimeter.

EUREKA
MATH™

Lesson 26:    Use rectangles to draw a robot with specified perimeter
              measurements, and reason about the different areas that may be
              produced.

©2015 Great Minds. eureka-math.org
G3-M7-SE-B4-1.3.1-01.2016

117

2. Each student in Mrs. Dutra's class draws a rectangle with whole number side lengths and a perimeter of 28 centimeters. Then, they find the area of each rectangle and create the table below.

| Area in Square Centimeters | Number of Students |
|---|---|
| 13 | 2 |
| 24 | 1 |
| 33 | 3 |
| 40 | 5 |
| 45 | 4 |
| 48 | 2 |
| 49 | 2 |

a. Give two examples from Mrs. Dutra's class to show how it is possible to have different areas for rectangles that have the same perimeter.

b. Did any students in Mrs. Dutra's class draw a square? Explain how you know.

c. What are the side lengths of the rectangle that most students in Mrs. Dutra's class made with a perimeter of 28 centimeters?

Lesson 26: Use rectangles to draw a robot with specified perimeter measurements, and reason about the different areas that may be produced.

©2015 Great Minds. eureka-math.org
G3-M7-SE-B4-1.3.1-01.2016

EUREKA MATH

Name _____   Date _____

**Part A:** I reviewed _____'s robot.

1.  Use the chart below to evaluate your friend's robot. Measure the width and length of each rectangle. Then, calculate the perimeter. Record that information in the chart below. If your measurements differ from those listed on the project, put a star by the letter of the rectangle.

| Rectangle | Width and Length | Student's Perimeter | Required Perimeter |
|---|---|---|---|
| A | _____ cm by _____ cm | | 14 cm |
| B | _____ cm by _____ cm | | 14 cm |
| C | _____ cm by _____ cm | | 18 cm |
| D | _____ cm by _____ cm | | 18 cm |
| E | _____ cm by _____ cm | | 28 cm |
| F | _____ cm by _____ cm | | 16 cm |
| G | _____ cm by _____ cm | | 8 cm |
| H | _____ cm by _____ cm | | |
| I | _____ cm by _____ cm | | |

   **Lesson 27:**   Use rectangles to draw a robot with specified perimeter measurements, and reason about the different areas that may be produced.    **119**

©2015 Great Minds. eureka-math.org
G3-M7-SE-B4-1.3.1-01.2016

2. Is the perimeter of the robot's body double that of the arm? Show calculations below.

3. Is the perimeter of the robot's neck half the perimeter of the head? Show calculations below.

Lesson 27: Use rectangles to draw a robot with specified perimeter measurements, and reason about the different areas that may be produced.

EUREKA
MATH™

**Part B:** I reviewed _____'s robot environment.

4.  Use the chart below to evaluate your friend's robot environment. Measure the width and length of each rectangle. Then, calculate the perimeter. Use your string to measure the perimeters of nonrectangular items. Record that information in the chart below. If your measurements differ from those listed on the project, put a star by the letter of the shape.

| Item | Width and Length | Student's Perimeter | Required Perimeter |
|------|------------------|---------------------|--------------------|
| J | | | About 25 cm |
| K | _____ cm by _____ cm | | 82 cm |
| L | | | About 30 cm |
| M | _____ cm by _____ cm | | 30 cm |
| N | | | About 20 cm |
| O | _____ cm by _____ cm | | 20 cm |
| P | | | |
| Q | | | |

©2015 Great Minds. eureka-math.org
G3-M7-SE-B4-1.3.1-01.2016

This page  intentionally left  blank

Name _____     Date _____

Record the perimeters and areas of the rectangles in the chart on the next page.

6 cm

1 cm

6 cm   A

8 cm

4 cm   B

C

11 cm

5 cm

5 cm   D

8 cm

2 cm   E

6 cm

4 cm   F

EUREKA MATH™

1.  Find the area and perimeter of each rectangle.

| Rectangle | Width and Length | Perimeter | Area |
|---|---|---|---|
| A | _____ cm by _____ cm | | |
| B | _____ cm by _____ cm | | |
| C | _____ cm by _____ cm | | |
| D | _____ cm by _____ cm | | |
| E | _____ cm by _____ cm | | |
| F | _____ cm by _____ cm | | |

2.  What do you notice about the perimeters of Rectangles A, B, and C?

3.  What do you notice about the perimeters of Rectangles D, E, and F?

4.  Which two rectangles are squares?  Which square has the greater perimeter?

Lesson 27:    Use rectangles to draw a robot with specified perimeter
measurements, and reason about the different areas that may be
produced.

©2015 Great Minds. eureka-math.org
G3-M7-SE-B4-1.3.1-01.2016

EUREKA
MATH™

Name __Sample_____ Date _____

**Part A:** I reviewed __Student A__ 's robot.

Use the chart below to evaluate your friend's robot. Measure the lengths and widths of each rectangle. Then calculate the perimeter. Record that information in the table below. If your measurements differ from those listed on the project, put a star by the letter of the rectangle.

| Rectangle | Width and Length | Student's Perimeter | Required Perimeter |
|---|---|---|---|
| A | __2__ cm by __5__ cm | 2cm + 2cm + 5cm + 5cm = 14cm | 14 cm |
| B | __2__ cm by __5__ cm | | 14 cm |
| C | __2__ cm by __7__ cm | | 18 cm |
| D | __2__ cm by __7__ cm | | 18 cm |
| E | __6__ cm by __8__ cm | | 28 cm |
| F | __4__ cm by __4__ cm | | 16 cm |
| G | __2__ cm by __2__ cm | | 8 cm |
| H | _____ cm by _____ cm | | |
| I | _____ cm by _____ cm | | |

sample Problem Set

**Lesson 27:** Use rectangles to draw a robot with specified perimeter measurements, and reason about the different areas that may be produced.

125

©2015 Great Minds. eureka-math.org
G3-M7-SE-B4-1.3.1-01.2016

This page intentionally left blank

Name _____     Date _____

1.  Gia measures her rectangular garden and finds the width is 9 yards and the length is 7 yards.

    a.  Estimate to draw Gia's garden, and label the side lengths.

    b.  What is the area of Gia's garden?

    c.  What is the perimeter of Gia's garden?

2.  Elijah draws a square that has side lengths of 8 centimeters.

    a.  Estimate to draw Elijah's square, and label the side lengths.

    b.  What is the area of Elijah's square?

    c.  What is the perimeter of Elijah's square?

**Lesson 28:**   Solve a variety of word problems involving area and perimeter using all
four operations.

127

©2015 Great Minds. eureka-math.org
G3-M7-SE-B4-1.3.1-01.2016

d. Elijah connects three of these squares to make one long rectangle. What is the perimeter of this rectangle?

3. The area of Mason's rectangular painting is 72 square inches. The width of the painting is 8 inches.

a. Estimate to draw Mason's painting, and label the side lengths.

b. What is the length of the painting?

c. What is the perimeter of Mason's painting?

d. Mason's mom hangs the painting on a wall that already has two of Mason's other paintings. The areas of the other paintings are 64 square inches and 81 square inches. What is the total area of the wall that is covered with Mason's paintings?

Lesson 28: Solve a variety of word problems involving area and perimeter using all four operations.

©2015 Great Minds. eureka-math.org
G3-M7-SE-B4-1.3.1-01.2016

EUREKA MATH

4.  The perimeter of Jillian's rectangular bedroom is 34 feet.  The length of her bedroom is 9 feet.

    a.  Estimate to draw Jillian's bedroom, and label the side lengths.

    b.  What is the width of Jillian's bedroom?

    c.  What is the area of Jillian's bedroom?

    d.  Jillian has a 4-foot by 6-foot rug in her room.  What is the area of the floor that is not covered by the rug?

EUREKA
MATH™

Lesson 28:   Solve a variety of word problems involving area and perimeter using all
             four operations.

©2015 Great Minds. eureka-math.org
G3-M7-SE-B4-1.3.1-01.2016

129

This page intentionally left blank

Name _____     Date _____

1.  Carl draws a square that has side lengths of 7 centimeters.

    a.  Estimate to draw Carl's square, and label the side lengths.

    b.  What is the area of Carl's square?

    c.  What is the perimeter of Carl's square?

    d.  Carl draws two of these squares to make one long rectangle.  What is the perimeter of this rectangle?

 EUREKA MATH™

Lesson 28:   Solve a variety of word problems involving area and perimeter using all four operations.

131

©2015 Great Minds. eureka-math.org
G3-M7-SE-B4-1.3.1-01.2016

2.  Mr. Briggs puts food for the class party on a rectangular table.  The table has a perimeter of 18 feet and a width of 3 feet.

    a.  Estimate to draw the table, and label the side lengths.

    b.  What is the length of the table?

    c.  What is the area of the table?

    d.  Mr. Briggs puts three of these tables together side by side to make 1 long table.  What is the area of the long table?

**Lesson 28:**      Solve a variety of word problems involving area and perimeter using all
                            four operations.

                EUREKA
                MATH™

©2015 Great Minds. eureka-math.org
G3-M7-SE-B4-1.3.1-01.2016

Name _____   Date _____

1.  Kyle puts two rectangles together to make the L-shaped figure below.  He measures some of the side lengths and records them as shown.

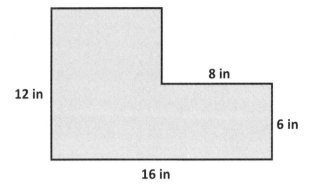

    a.  Find the perimeter of Kyle's shape.

    b.  Find the area of Kyle's shape.

    c.  Kyle makes two copies of the L-shaped figure to create the rectangle shown below.  Find the perimeter of the rectangle.

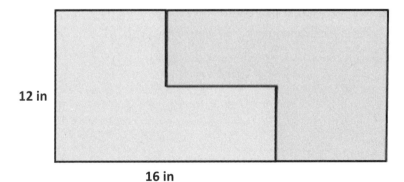

©2015 Great Minds. eureka-math.org
G3-M7-SE-B4-1.3.1-01.2016

2.  Jeremiah and Hayley use a piece of rope to mark a square space for their booth at the science fair.  The area of their space is 49 square feet.  What is the length of the rope that Jeremiah and Hayley use if they leave a 3-foot opening so they can get in and out of the space?

3.  Vivienne draws four identical rectangles as shown below to make a new, larger rectangle.  The perimeter of one of the small rectangles is 18 centimeters, and the width is 6 centimeters.  What is the perimeter of the new, larger rectangle?

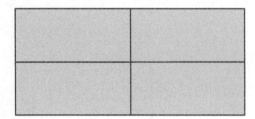

4.  A jogging path around the outside edges of a rectangular playground measures 48 yards by 52 yards.  Maya runs $3\frac{1}{2}$ laps on the jogging path.  What is the total number of yards Maya runs?

Solve a variety of word problems involving area and perimeter using al
          four operations.

EUREKA
MATH

Name _____  Date _____

1.  Katherine puts two squares together to make the rectangle below.  The side lengths of the squares measure 8 inches.

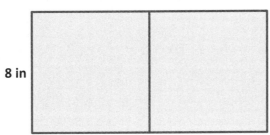

8 in

a.  What is the perimeter of the rectangle Katherine made with her 2 squares?

b.  What is the area of Katherine's rectangle?

c.  Katherine decides to draw another rectangle of the same size.  What is the area of the new, larger rectangle?

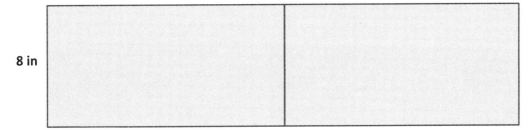

8 in

EUREKA MATH™

Lesson 29:  Solve a variety of word problems involving area and perimeter using al four operations.

135

©2015 Great Minds. eureka-math.org
G3-M7-SE-B4-1.3.1-01.2016

2.  Daryl draws 6 equal-sized rectangles as shown below to make a new, larger rectangle.  The area of one of the small rectangles is 12 square centimeters, and the width of the small rectangle is 4 centimeters.

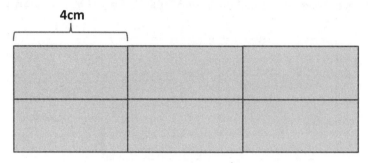

4cm

a.  What is the perimeter of Daryl's new rectangle?

b.  What is the area of Daryl's new rectangle?

3.  The recreation center soccer field measures 35 yards by 65 yards.  Chris dribbles the soccer ball around the perimeter of the field 4 times.  What is the total number of yards Chris dribbles the ball?

**Lesson 29:**        Solve a variety of word problems involving area and perimeter using al four operations.

EUREKA
MATH™

Name _____   Date _____

Use this form to critique your classmate's problem-solving work.

| Classmate: | | Problem Number: | |
|---|---|---|---|
| Strategies My Classmate Used: | | | |
| Things My Classmate Did Well: | | | |
| Suggestions for Improvement: | | | |
| Strategies I Would Like to Try Based on My Classmate's Work: | | | |

**Lesson 30:**   Share and critique peer strategies for problem solving.

137

©2015 Great Minds. eureka-math.org
G3-M7-SE-B4-1.3.1-01.2016

This page intentionally left blank

Name _____ Date _____

Use this form to critique Student A's problem-solving work on the next page.

| Student: | Student A | Problem Number: | |
|---|---|---|---|
| Strategies Student A Used: | | | |
| Things Student A Did Well: | | | |
| Suggestions for Improvement: | | | |
| Strategies I Would Like to Try Based on Student A's Work: | | | |

This page  intentionally left  blank

Name _____ **STUDENT A** _____        Date _____

1.  Katherine puts 2 squares together to make the rectangle below. The side lengths of the squares measure 8 inches.

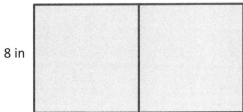

8 in

a.  What is the perimeter of Katherine's rectangle?

8in  8in

8in                8in

8in  8in

P = 6 × 8 in
P = 48 in
The perimeter is 48 inches.

b.  What is the area of Katherine's rectangle?

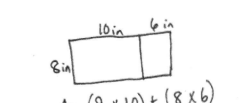

10in  6 in

8in

A = (8 × 10) + (8 × 6)
A = 80 + 48
A = 128
The area is 128 sq in.

c. Katherine draws 2 of the rectangles in Problem 1 side by side. Her new, larger rectangle is shown below. What is the area of the new, larger rectangle?

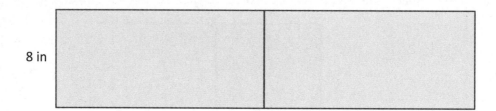

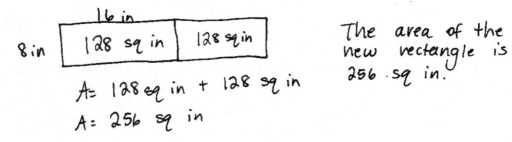

A = 128 sq in + 128 sq in

A = 256 sq in

The area of the new rectangle is 256 sq in.

**Lesson 30:**   Share and critique peer strategies for problem solving.

©2015 Great Minds. eureka-math.org
G3-M7-SE-B4-1.3.1-01.2016

EUREKA
MATH™

**Student A**

7ft

7ft | A=49 sq ft |

$P = 7ft + 7ft + 7ft + 7ft$
$P = 4 \times 7ft$
$P = 28ft$

$7 \times 7 = 49$

28ft

r ft

3ft

$r = 28 - 3$
$r = 25$
The total length of the rope is 25 feet.

---

**Student B**

7ft

A=49 sq ft | 7ft

$\_\_ \times \_\_ = 49$
$7 \times 7 = 49$

7ft

7ft | 7ft
4ft  3ft opening

$7ft + 7ft + 7ft + 4ft$

$3 \times 7ft = 21ft$

$21 ft + 4ft$
$25 ft$

The length of the rope is 25 feet.

---

**Student C**

Area = 49 sq ft
Possible rectangles:

49 ft
1 ft

7 ft
7 ft
square

7ft

7ft | 7ft
7ft

$P = 4 \times 7ft$
$P = 28 ft$

$28 ft - 3 ft = 25 ft$
The length of the rope is 25 ft.

---

student work sample images

This page intentionally left blank

Name _____ Date _____

Use this form to analyze your classmate's representations of one-half shaded.

| Square (letter) | Does this square show one-half shaded? | Explain why or why not. | Describe changes to make so the square shows one-half shaded. |
|---|---|---|---|
|  |  |  |  |
|  |  |  |  |
|  |  |  |  |
|  |  |  |  |

Lesson 31: Explore and create unconventional representations of one-half.

145

©2015 Great Minds. eureka-math.org
G3-M7-SE-B4-1.3.1-01.2016

This page intentionally left blank

Name _____     Date _____

1.  Use the rectangle below to answer Problem 1(a–d).

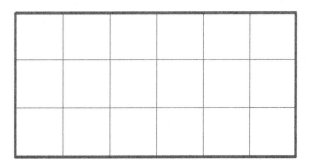

a.  What is the area of the rectangle in square units?

b.  What is the area of half of the rectangle in square units?

c.  Shade in half of the rectangle above.  Be creative with your shading!

d.  Explain how you know you shaded in half of the rectangle.

2. During math class, Arthur, Emily, and Gia draw a shape and then shade one-half of it.  Analyze each student's work.  Determine if each student was correct or not, and explain your thinking.

| Student | Drawing | Your Analysis |
|---------|---------|---------------|
| Arthur | | |
| Emily | | |
| Gia | | |

3. Shade the grid below to show two different ways of shading half of each shape.

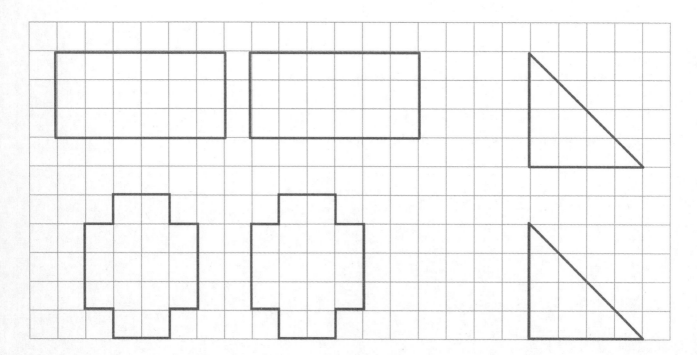

Explore and create unconventional representations of one-half.

EUREKA
MATH

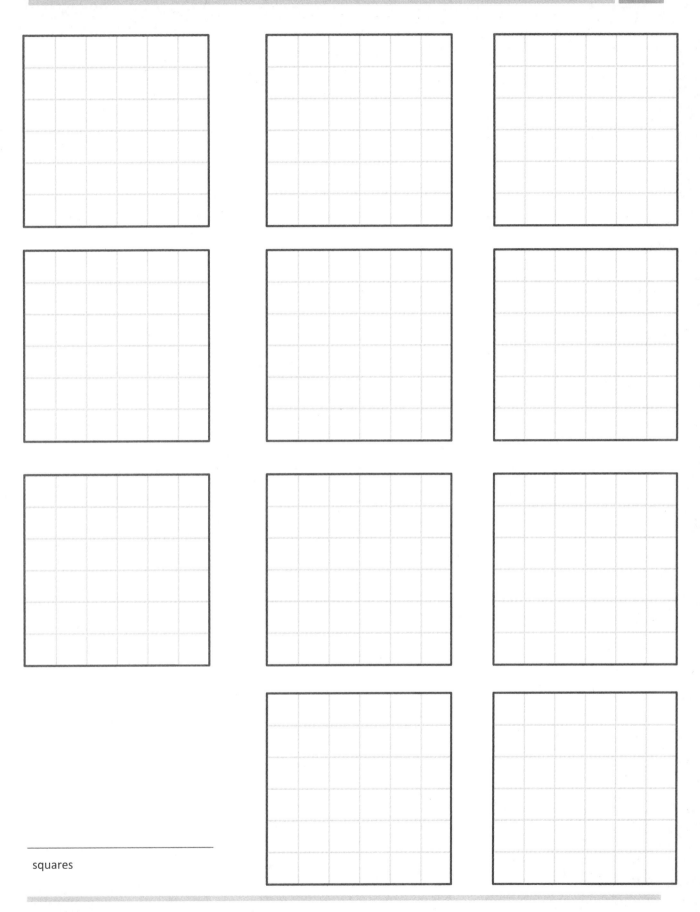

squares

Lesson 31:      Explore and create unconventional representations of one-half.

EUREKA
MATH™

149

©2015 Great Minds. eureka-math.org
G3-M7-SE-B4-1.3.1-01.2016

This page intentionally left blank

Name _____    Date _____

1. Look at the circles you shaded today.  Glue a circle that is about one-half shaded in the space below.

 

 

    a.  Explain the strategy you used to shade in one-half of your circle.

 

    b.  Is your circle exactly one-half shaded?  Explain your answer.

 

2. Julian shades 4 circles as shown below.

      Circle A          Circle B        Circle C        Circle D

    a.  Write the letters of the circles that are about one-half shaded.

b. Choose one circle from your answer to Part (a), and explain how you know it's about one-half shaded.

Circle _____

c. Choose one circle that you did not list in Part (a), and explain how it could be changed so that it is about one-half shaded.

Circle _____

3. Read the clues to help you shade the circle below.

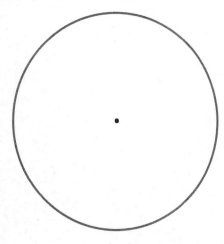

a. Divide the circle into 4 equal parts.

b. Shade in 2 parts.

c. Erase a small circle from each shaded part.

d. Estimate to draw and shade 2 circles in the unshaded parts that are the same size as the circles you erased in Part (c).

4. Did you shade in one-half of the circle in Problem 3? How do you know?

EUREKA MATH™

©2015 Great Minds. eureka-math.org
G3-M7-SE-B4-1.3.1-01.2016

Name _____ Date _____

1. Estimate to finish shading the circles below so that each circle is about one-half shaded.

a.

b.
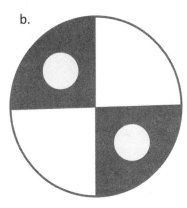

c.
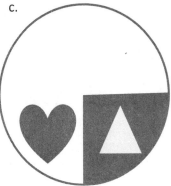

2. Choose one of the circles in Problem 1, and explain how you know it's about one-half shaded.

Circle _____

3. Can you say the circles in Problem 1 are exactly one-half shaded? Why or why not?

EUREKA MATH

Lesson 32: Explore and create unconventional representations of one-half.

153

4. Marissa and Jake shade in circles as shown below.

**Marissa's Circle**                     **Jake's Circle**

a. Whose circle is about one-half shaded? How do you know?

b. Explain how the circle that is not one-half shaded can be changed so that it is one-half shaded.

5. Estimate to shade about one-half of each circle below in an unusual way.

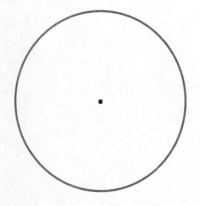 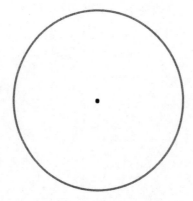 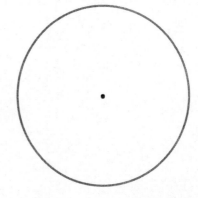

     **Lesson 32:**     Explore and create unconventional representations of one-half.

Name _____ Date _____

List some games we played today in the chart below. Place a check mark in the box that shows how you felt about your level of fluency as you played each activity. Check off the last column if you would like to practice this activity over the summer.

| Activity | I still need some practice with my facts. | I am fluent. | I would like to put this in my summer activity book. |
|---|---|---|---|
| 1. | | | |
| 2. | | | |
| 3. | | | |
| 4. | | | |
| 5. | | | |
| 6. | | | |
| 7. | | | |
| 8. | | | |

Lesson 33:     Solidify fluency with Grade 3 skills.

155

This page intentionally left blank

Name _____     Date _____

Teach a family member your favorite fluency game from class.  Record information about the game you taught below.

Name of the game: _____

_____

Materials used: _____

_____

Name of the person you taught to play: _____

Describe what it was like to teach the game.  Was it easy?  Hard?  Why? _____

_____

_____

_____

Will you play the game together again?  Why or why not? _____

_____

_____

Was the game as fun to play at home as in class?  Why or why not? _____

_____

_____

This page  intentionally left  blank

Name _____   Date _____

Complete a math activity each day.  To track your progress, color the box after you finish.

### Summer Math Review:  Weeks 1–5

| | Monday | Tuesday | Wednesday | Thursday | Friday |
|---|---|---|---|---|---|
| Week 1 | Do jumping jacks as you count by twos from 2 to 20 and back. | Play a game from your Summer Practice booklet. | Use your tangram pieces to make a picture of your summer break. | Time how long it takes you to do a specific chore, like making the bed. See if you can do it faster the next day. | Complete a Sprint. |
| Week 2 | Do squats as you count by threes from 3 to 30 and back. | Play a game from your Summer Practice booklet. | Collect data about your family's or friends' favorite type of music. Show it on a bar graph.  What did you discover from your graph? | Read a recipe. What fractions does the recipe use? | Complete a Multiply by Pattern Sheet. |
| Week 3 | Hop on one foot as you count by fours from 4 to 40 and back. | Create a multiplication and/or division math game.  Then, play the game with a partner. | Measure the widths of different leaves from the same tree to the nearest quarter inch.  Then, draw a line plot of your data.  Do you notice a pattern? | Read the weight in grams of different food items in your kitchen.  Round the weights to the nearest 10 or 100 grams. | Complete a Sprint. |
| Week 4 | Bounce a ball as you count by 5 minutes to 1 hour and then to the half hour and quarter hours. | Find, draw, and/or create different objects to show one-fourth. | Go on a shape scavenger hunt. Find as many quadrilaterals in your neighborhood or house as you can. | Find the sum and difference of 453 mL and 379 mL. | Complete a Multiply by Pattern Sheet. |
| Week 5 | Do arm swings as you count by sixes from 6 to 60 and back. | Draw and label a floor plan of your house. | Measure the perimeter of the room where you sleep in inches. Then, calculate the area. | Use a stopwatch to measure how fast you can run 50 meters.  Do it 3 times.  What was your fastest time? | Complete a Sprint. |

Name _____    Date _____

Complete a math activity each day.  To track your progress, color the box after you finish.

### Summer Math Review:  Weeks 6–10

|  | Monday | Tuesday | Wednesday | Thursday | Friday |
|---|---|---|---|---|---|
| **Week 6** | Alternate counting with a friend or family member by sevens from 7 to 70 and back. | Play a game from your Summer Practice booklet. | Write a story problem for 7 × 6. | Solve 15 × 4.  Draw a model to show your thinking. | Complete a Multiply by Pattern Sheet. |
| **Week 7** | Jump forward and back as you count by eights from 8 to 80 and back. | Play a game from your Summer Practice booklet. | Use string to measure the perimeter of circular items in your house to the nearest quarter inch. | Build a 4 by 6 array with objects from your house.  Write 2 multiplication and 2 division sentences for your array. | Complete a Sprint. |
| **Week 8** | Do arm crosses as you count by nines from 9 to 90 and back.<br><br>Teach someone the nines finger trick. | Create a multiplication and/or division math game.  Then, play the game with a partner. | Write a story problem for 72 ÷ 8. | Measure or find the capacity in milliliters of different liquids in your kitchen.  Round each to the nearest 10 or 100 milliliters. | Complete a Multiply by Pattern Sheet. |
| **Week 9** | Jump rope as you count up by tens from 280 to 370 and back down. | Find, draw, and/or create different objects to show one-third. | Go on a shape scavenger hunt.  Find as many triangles and hexagons in your neighborhood as you can. | Measure the weight of different produce at the grocery store.  What unit did you measure in?  What are the lightest and heaviest objects you weighed? | Complete a Sprint. |
| **Week 10** | Count by sixes starting at 48.  Count as high as you can in one minute. | Draw and label a floor plan of your dream tree house. | Find the perimeter of a different room in your house.  How much smaller or larger is it compared to the perimeter of the room where you sleep? | Show someone your strategy to solve 8 × 16. | Complete a Multiply by Pattern Sheet. |

       **Lesson 34:**     Create resource booklets to support fluency with Grade 3 skills.

This page intentionally left blank

This page intentionally left blank